Alaskan Oil: Costs and Supply

New Directions in Management and Economics

. . . a series of authoritative books for more effective decision-making . . .

Alaskan Oil:
Costs and Supply

M. A. Adelman
Paul G. Bradley
Charles A. Norman

PRAEGER PUBLISHERS
New York • Washington • London

PRAEGER PUBLISHERS
111 Fourth Avenue, New York, N.Y. 10003, U.S.A.
5, Cromwell Place, London S.W.7, England

Published in the United States of America in 1971
by Praeger Publishers, Inc.

© 1971 by Praeger Publishers, Inc.

Library of Congress Catalog Card Number: 72–122087

Printed in the United States of America

Contents

Introduction

This volume contains four independently written studies of very unequal length; yet they form a book and not a collection. Three are concerned with the cost of developing and transporting crude oil from a great new field; the fourth with the cost of finding more new fields. The three should be examined for points of agreement and disagreement on method and substance; the fourth crowns the work by inviting the reader to look up from the ground and off at the horizon.

The oil industry, to a degree matched by few others, lives in the future and calculates with expected, not current, variables. Yet the forecasts must be based on current knowledge. Hence one must begin by figuring a cost or other number from available scanty bits of imperfect evidence, knowing well that the job must be redone and again redone as more data come to light. Indeed, the most important result of any such early reckoning may be to indicate what additional data are needed. A newly discovered pool means a decision on what to invest in development, if anything. The oilman must guess at dimensions, structure, and composition to calculate the investment needed for any given number of barrels of daily production, and he must look to an expected price. If he goes ahead, then as development proceeds, more wells are drilled, much more is known, and all is recalculated. Early or late, he probably will consider the chances of finding more pools, better or poorer, on the same geological structure.

These papers, based altogether on outside information, the public record available to all, appraise oil development on the North Slope of Alaska, as seen in a particular year. Decline rates and producing rates, and the key figure of investment per daily barrel of initial output, are estimated by sifting out what is in the public domain and "plugging in" what may be presumed from experience elsewhere. The first three papers evaluate what was then known of the new pool (perhaps pools) in a new field (perhaps fields) on the Alaskan North Slope. The study by Charles A. Norman is a painstaking evaluation by an engineer-manager-economist, who may contest that last title, but has fairly earned it. It has been revised in the light of information made available after the $900 million Alaskan lease sale in September, 1969. The Task Force estimates and my own paper are treated here as documents and left as they were in August, 1969, before the sale.

Each paper serves as both criticism and confirmation of the others. It is particularly interesting to see what one takes as given and another explores more intensively. Norman carefully adapts the theory of finance to approximate the rate of return of Atlantic Richfield and Jersey Standard; the other papers are content to assume rates of return and let the reader substitute his own if he wishes. The Task Force assumes the use of the Northwest Passage, and the existence of the Jones Act; the other papers put the first aside as still an unknown, and treat the second as a special political addition to cost.

Much that is now common knowledge could then only be guessed at. Certain possibilities are still too complex even for Norman's careful analysis. In the long run, the very large gas resources at Prudhoe Bay will lower oil development-production costs. But in the short run, the oil companies may not be permitted to vent the gas but may be required to return it to the deposit, thus increasing development cost. To balance the small early penalty against the large future benefit, we need to know more than we do now. These three papers are content to leave gas aside, or rather to guess that its present value is a small but incalculable plus, a reduction in real cost.

Curiously enough, these three essays are at one and the same time (1) a radical departure from the type of cost calculation usually published by industry and government sources and (2) altogether consistent with industry practice, in fact a simple adaptation of discounted cash flow. The basic approach is traditional economics: cost is defined as *supply price,* i.e., that net payment per unit of output which would just suffice to call forth a given amount of output. It is only a refinement or perhaps only a consistent statement of what oilmen do, a process with many similarities to what happens in other industries—and a few important differences.

In economic analysis the name of the game is understanding, not advocacy or justification. The basic rule is the reproducible calculation. Whether or not to play the game is a matter of taste, but tastes and customs change. Time was when a spokesman needed only to assure members of Congress or the press that "my people tell me that" the cost or price or whatever was such and such a figure. Thenceforth it was gospel. Today it is merely the unsup-. ported guess of a man who wants to sell us something. But even more important than the descent from the pedestal is the realization that a "cost" only has meaning if it is comparable with price and relevant to an investment decision. Hence a very popular idea, "replacement cost," is of no interest or application because it has no bearing on investing for development or for exploration. An oil pool is or is not worth developing, new acreage is or is not worth exploring, regardless of what was once spent to find the first reservoir: bygones are bygones.

One disagreement, perhaps, is to be seen among the first three studies. The Task Force report pushes the principle of cost as supply price to an extreme which the two other authors do not follow. It makes the supply price high enough to cover current federal and local tax rates. The other two papers treat the tax as zero in order to arrive at a figure net after tax which will make the Prudhoe Bay pool just barely worth exploitation. They assume that prices and taxes will be adapted to costs and estimate only one of the factors—cost—among the several which will together determine prices, outputs, profits, and taxes.

On the whole, the field development cost estimates are too high, but they are also too simple. Already there appears to be at Prudhoe Bay a limestone not worth producing, a sand good for 1,300 barrels daily per well, and the Prudhoe Bay sand itself, good for over 20,000. (By way of comparison, production per well per day in Kuwait is 3,400, in Iran 16,000, in Iraq 14,000, in Saudia Arabia 6,700, in Libya 3,500.) How many wells per "pad" can be maintained at such a rate, and how many will be drilled before well interference brings it down, depends on the size of the pool, which, in a manner typical of pools, seems to be expanding.

By the time this book is in print more will be known. What will not be out of date is the method, and the reader will be well advised to look carefully at Norman's sensitivity analysis and apply it to the other studies as well.

None of the studies forecasts the price of North Slope oil, or even suggests any such price. This will come as something of a surprise to readers who know the two documents only from press reports. ("Price" means a sum paid in an arm's length transaction, not a fiction posted to set a tax.)

Whether Prudhoe cost will have much to do with the price of Alaskan oil depends on how many more and what kind of discoveries take place. But of course there is an interaction. Because Prudhoe Bay oil is very cheap, there has been a rush into the North Slope. It is not the promise of "finding huge reserves" which draws exploration, but rather the promise of finding large amounts of oil which can be *developed into reserves* at a very low cost. Against large hoped-for profits, operators are willing to give away some small fraction in hard cash as lease bonus payments. Some have paid far more than they ever will earn out of the development investment; for some the bonus and royalties will be only a small fraction of profits.

That is the nature of oil exploration. Bradley's essay. is based on the proposition that finding cost has nothing to do with adding up, after the fact, what was spent to gain the knowledge of an oil deposit. For such a figure has nothing to do with the decision to explore or the decision to develop. The only exploration cost that has any relevance is a comparison of what must be spent with the mathematical expectation of what one will find. His paper is an admirable summary of the method of calculating those probabilities, and an introduction to its application in a new area. One enters on the basis of experience in the nearest comparable area or average of comparable areas. This means, first and foremost, dismissing the lower forty-eight of the U.S. states, whose dismal exploratory record since the 1950's is no basis for prediction elsewhere. If it were a basis, "elsewhere" would be a place to avoid. But starting with these vaguely figured odds, one substitutes knowledge of the new area as fast as it is gained. Then one can make some first calculation of the tradeoff between the increasing cost of more intensive development in the known fields (or what has been called Maximum Economic Finding Cost) and the chancy but perhaps very low finding cost as one looks at a new exploration province.

Here then are four studies of the Alaskan North Slope as it looked late in 1969. The insights and the errors will both have something to teach those interested in Alaskan oil, as well as those interested in energy economics in the widest sense.

April, 1970

Significance of Shifts in World Oil Supplies, with Special Reference to Alaska

M. A. Adelman *

The pattern of world oil supplies has changed significantly over the past 30 years. In the 1940's, the center of gravity of known reserves shifted from the Western to the Eastern Hemisphere and leadership in production duly followed. Countries that were nonproducers at one date were major supply sources 10 years later. The outstanding example is of course Libya. These changing patterns are summed up in Table 1. What newcomers will make their mark over the next 10 years, we cannot say. Nigeria will undoubtedly be several times as important as now, and probably Indonesia as well. Alaska too will be a major producer. But as the industry is multiplied in size, it becomes more stable. The center of gravity is harder to displace, and it will not return to the Western Hemisphere in the next 20 years.

* M. A. Adelman is Professor of Economics at the Massachusetts Institute of Technology.

13

Table 1

World Crude Oil Production and Reserves
Principal Countries 1938-1968

	1938 Produc-tion TBD	1938 Re-serves Bill. bbl	1948 Produc-tion TBD	1948 Re-serves Bill. bbl	1958 Produc-tion TBD	1958 Re-serves Bill. bbl	1968 Produc-tion TBD	1968 Re-serves Bill. bbl
North America								
U. S.	3475	17	6000	27	7520	37	10,610	39
Canada	20	—	34	—	465	4	1,165	10
Mexico	105	—	160	1	255	3	430	6
Total	3600	—	6194	28	8240	43	12,205	55
Caribbean and South America								
Venezuela	515	3	1339	9	2605	17	3,620	16
Total	720	—	2005	10	3070	20	4,690	23
Middle East								
Iran	210	2	520	7	825	33	2,835	54
Iraq	90	1	71	5	725	25	1,505	28
Kuwait	—	—	127	11	1395	60	2,630	69
S. Arabia	—	—	390	9	1005	47	3,040	77
Other	20	—	30	1	295	9	1,595	42
Total	320	—	1139	33	4245	174	11,605	271
Africa								
Algeria	—	—	—	—	10	3	920	7
Libya	—	—	—	—	—	—	2,600	30
Nigeria	—	—	—	—	5	—	[140]*	4
Other	5	—	37	—	70	1	: 400	3
Total	5	—	37	—	85	4	4,060	45
S.E. Asia								
Indonesia	150	1	87	1	330	9	550	9
Total	170	—	152	1	430	10	675	14
USSR et al.	720	4	727	5	2585	28	6,785	56
World Total **	5585	30	9880	77	18,945	279	40,235	465

* March 1967 = 570 TBD.
** Includes countries not shown individually.

TBD = thousand barrels daily.

SOURCES: *Production:* U.S. and Canada: Bureau of Mines *Yearbook.* Natural gas liquids included. Other countries: 1938, 1958, 1968 *Oil & Gas Journal* annual supplement on international oil. 1948, *World Oil,* "International Outlook" issue, 1956.

Reserves—U.S. & Canada: API *Proved Reserves* annual. Natural gas liquids included. Other countries: 1948 to 1968, *Oil & Gas Journal* annual supplement on international oil. Venezuela includes natural gas liquids. 1938, rough estimates calculated from BP *Statistical Review* (1957), and *History of the Petroleum Administration for War* (1945).

A backward glance at what has happened tells us little about how and why. But the very fact of swift change should warn us that there must have been surprises en route. Those tiny 1938 Persian Gulf proved reserves reflected 30 years of experience. In 1944 a prediction was made that they would in years to come be about 13–18 billion barrels; consider in this light the 1968 prediction of 5–10 billion barrels for Alaska.

Change and uncertainty form an underlying theme in the process of shifting oil supplies, but they are obstacles to movement, not inducements. Oil companies subject themselves to uncertainty in their search for profit. Great new oil provinces are rapidly opened because they are cheaper. There has always been enough oil in the old provinces, and there still is, but at a higher cost.

We can unite the two themes of uncertainty and cost. An analogy may help: a boat creeping forward in a fog. At each point, soundings tell the depth of the bottom at that point but give only faint indication of depth a few yards away, let alone longer distances. In oil production, development cost in known pools can be calculated with tolerable accuracy even on the basis of incomplete data. What we do not know is the cost of finding and then developing fields now unknown. We will now try to give these ideas some precision in order to look backward and forward.

CONCEPT AND MEASURE OF "RESERVES"

Just as production is only one year's drain of the much bigger amount, reserves, so also reserves are a fraction of a much larger total, oil-in-place. At the end of 1968, about 388 billion barrels of crude oil had been discovered in reservoirs in the United States, 87 billion barrels had been produced, and 31 billion were current "proved reserves." [1] In other words, 118 billion had been quarried out for proved reserves, developed for eventual production, and mostly produced. Of some 300 billion barrels remaining underground today, the total ultimately produced could be several times the 30 billion barrels of current proved reserves. If, for example, the average recovery factor could be raised as high as 50 percent, that would be 194 billion of the original oil-in-place, of which 87 have already been produced, and 31 developed into proved reserves, leaving another 76 billion of potential reserves. How much or little is ultimately developed depends on costs and prices.

The frequent cirticisms of reserve statistics as being too "conservative" are really a demand for a forecast of how much oil-in-place will some day be converted into proved reserves and produced. While such forecasts are perfectly legitimate, and are occasionally made—the case of Alaska will soon be discussed—they are a different kind of concept.

Proved reserves, as estimated by the American Petroleum Institute–American Gas Association (API-AGA),[2] are those quantities recoverable "with reasonable certainty . . . under existing economic and operating conditions." This covers little beyond facilities already in place: the drilled portion of a reservoir and the adjoining area judged productive on the basis of "available geological and engineering data." Reserves coming from application of improved recovery techniques are included as proved reserves only if the facilities have already been installed or at the very least there has been "successful testing by a pilot project." Proved reserves are that small part of oil-in-place which has been developed for production by the drilling and connecting of wells and associated facilities: the total of planned production from all facilities already installed and paid for.[3]

The ratio of proved reserves to annual production in the United States has slowly declined for many years. The producing industry has been able to reduce the shelf inventory it must carry. The ratio has no deeper significance, and is no warning of scarcity. Proved reserves *at any given time* are quite distinct from forecasts of what will be made into reserves *later*.[4] The great discovery in northern Alaska was said in June, 1968, to contain between 5 and 10 billion barrels. But the API-AGA, in crediting the North Slope with no reserves as of the end of 1968, was simply being consistent with its principle of counting only developed reserves. The Alaska estimate was a *forecast of the proved reserves which were expected to be developed*. Eight months later, in early 1969, there was in effect an amended forecast when it was announced that a pipeline built from the area would have an ultimate capacity of 2 million barrels daily. This indicates roughly 15 billion barrels forthcoming in 20 years. To compare the 5 or 10 or 15 billion for Alaska with either the 31 billion proved U.S. reserves or with the 300 billion U.S. oil-in-place would be incorrect. The North Slope estimate is neither one of these because it was made for a different purpose.

THE PRESSURE OF INCREASING COSTS WITH INTENSIVE DEVELOPMENT

In order to maintain and expand production, oil companies must build new capacity and thereby create additional proved reserves. But the more intensively they develop known reservoirs to maintain or increase the rate of output, the more will they increase development investment costs and also current operating costs because of well interference, reduced pressure, and the need for applying increasing amounts of water or gas injection. Hence oil companies will not only keep chopping away at the oil-in-place in known reservoirs, but may try to find new pools. They can increase reserves in or around known reservoirs at increasing cost, or look to the more risky but potentially more rewarding search for a new pool outside the limits of the old. Most risky and most profitable (if it succeeds) is a new field wildcat. The definition of a field is blurred at best. One writer says simply: "I use the term 'field' to describe an aggregate of overlapping, contiguous, or superimposed pools." [5] Pools and fields result from some set of geological disturbances which may extend over a wide area, or form what is often called a "trend" or "basin," which may be thought of as being to a field what a field is to a pool.

The oil industry thus can keep on adding to its proved reserves for many years without ever finding a new field, indeed with zero or modest additions to oil-in-place. Since the early 1950's in the United States the productivity of exploration has dwindled rapidly. Few large fields have been found, and very little oil-in-place per unit of exploration expenditure. Yet improved technology has (at least through 1963) more than offset the increase in developing cost which would be inevitable under stationary conditions. [6]

RESERVE ESTIMATES OUTSIDE NORTH AMERICA

For many years the *Oil & Gas Journal* and *World Oil* have made reserve estimates from information furnished by companies operating in the field and checked against the opinion of neighbors and competitors. There is practically nothing on oil-in-place. A few years ago the president of Jersey Standard estimated about a trillion barrels of oil-in-place in the non-Communist world at the end of 1962. This would leave 623 billion outside the United States, as compared with 240 billion published reserves for that year.

It is hard to say how comparable these estimates are to those of the United States. There are conflicting indications, illustrated by a recent estimate. The Saudi Arabian government commissioned a study which estimated 1968 proved reserves in that country as 142 billion rather than the 84

billion reckoned by Aramco (a figure not strictly comparable with Table 1). This difference of professional opinion
among reservoir engineers is not nearly as great as it would
appear. Where oil-in-place is so great relative to current
production, a very small difference in the interpretation of
current production results must be multiplied by a huge
factor to estimate ultimate production from existing facilities. What the special estimate shows is that there is a huge
store of Persian Gulf oil-in-place which can be developed
into new proved reserves for years to come at current development costs or only a little higher.

ALASKA DISCOVERY IN CONTEXT

Suppose that about 10 billion barrels will enter into Alaskan proved reserves by the end of 1973. Compare this with
what happened in 1963-1968 in three large producing cen-
ters (see Table 2). In the United States about one-tenth
represented new discoveries, and the rest reflected develop-
ments from oil-in-place in fields already known.[7]

Table 2

Gross Reserve Additions, 1963-1968

	Persian Gulf–Africa	North America	Venezuela
Reserves: end-1968	315	49	15.5
end-1963	223	47	17.0
net increase	92	2	−1.5
cumulative interim production	21	20	6.2
total increase	113	22	4.7

SOURCE: *Oil & Gas Journal,* annual supplement, "World Wide Oil."

In Venezuela there was very little exploration during this
time, and one is probably safe in assuming that nearly all
of the new reserves came from previously known fields,
including of course new reservoirs in old fields. In the

Persian Gulf–Africa, doubtless the great bulk was from old fields, but one cannot say more.

Compared with the Persian Gulf–African fields, the expected Alaskan development is very small: in round percentages less than one-tenth of what was accomplished there in the 1963-1968 period, and doubtless an even smaller percentage of what will be developed through 1973. But it is more than twice the comparable total for Venezuela, and nearly half what was done for North America. Thus in comparing it with the U.S. market, where Alaskan oil will find its primary outlet, we can see that the first North Slope discovery taken by itself is already a very large part of the total.

The earlier part of this chapter shows why the impact will be much larger than this simple comparison suggests. First, Alaskan proved reserves will in time reach a much larger figure than any total estimated thus far. (1) The Prudhoe Bay reservoir (or reservoirs?) is not yet delimited. (2) New reservoirs will be found in the neighborhood of Prudhoe Bay, adding to reserves in that one field alone. (3) Big fields are rarely found without smaller fields in the same general area or on the same trend. Hence it is reasonable to expect that the Prudhoe Bay discovery will be the first installment, presumably but not necessarily the largest, in a stream of new pools and new fields, the ultimate size of which is unknown.

The second reason why the simple comparison of reserves tends to underestimate the importance of the Alaska discovery brings us to the basic reason why oil finding and oil development are undertaken: to produce oil at the largest profit. The more reserves are developed out of a pool, the higher the development cost, until it equals price and expansion ceases. Conversely, the lower development is, the greater the scope for expanding capacity and creating new reserves. Development costs, therefore, are what we need to know.

DEVELOPMENT COSTS OF PRUDHOE BAY OIL

The costs of developing North Slope oil will in a sense never be known until the fields finally shut down. But it is not too soon to do the exercise with what fragments of information are in the public domain. It will give us a sense of orders of magnitude, pinpoint the kinds of data needed, and show the sensitivity to error. Our estimates will be examined by those with better data, who can correct them. That is how knowledge accumulates. Moreover, some grievous exaggerations have begun to gain currency, which would require assumptions about the North Slope that nobody inside or outside the industry could support.

The definition of cost has been fully treated elsewhere; it is that amount which would just pay operating cost plus a barely sufficient return on the needed development investment.[8] The cost thus estimated is not a forecast price, still less a suggested price. The excess of price over cost is a return for exploration risk, over and above development risk. If the excess is small, that means exploration is not worthwhile.

Drilling costs per North Slope development well are said to be in the range of $1.5 to $2.0 million. The first wells cost about $4 million, but this covered the facilities—the airstrip, road, campsite, rig location—adequate for many more. Thereafter well costs should be less than $2 million, and perhaps less than $1.5 million, particularly because the need for haste in the early stages forced an additional outlay of about $500,000 per well, which will be saved in the future.[9] As a check: "Exploratory drilling on the North Slope might cost between six and seven times that done on land in California."[10] Onshore California wells in the depth range of 7.5 to 10.0 thousand feet cost $230,000 apiece (dry holes, $112,000),[11] which comes to $1.5 million per well.

Recent estimates of initial production per well per day are in the 10- to 20-thousand-barrel range.[12] An optimistic guess would therefore be about $100 per daily barrel, a less glowing one about $200, which we will use. Those with better numbers will of course substitute them. An adjustment is needed for development of dry holes, which outside the United States (not relevant to a producing area like Alaska) seem to vary between 5 and 25 percent. Let us assume the middle value of 15 percent. If a dry hole was to cost half as much as a producer, drilling outlays would be less by 7.5 percent, but output would be lower by 15 percent, so that investment per daily barrel needs to be increased by a factor of 1.088, to $218.[13]

The development investment per daily barrel is a capital sum, spent today for a stream of barrels tomorrow. Assume alternatively a decline rate of 5 percent, or 10 percent to allow for an extremely intensive development which is compensated by a high price.

As usual, the rate of return is a difficult number to estimate. The return on oil equity securities, i.e., dividends plus growth rate, divided by the price of the stock, is not theoretically wrong. But it is influenced by the risk in exploration, refining and marketing, all greater than in development-production. There would be reason to use no more than a 10-12 percent rate of return.[14] But alternatives of 15 percent and 20 percent are preferred. The higher rates serve as a catch-all for minor risk and cost factors that may have been omitted.[15]

The rate of return is practically the same before or after tax, and our use of it is highly conservative.[16] Moreover, we assume the field lasts only 20 years, and set at zero the benefits of any natural gas discoveries.

Then at 15 percent rate of return and 5 percent decline, the capital cost per barrel is 11.5 cents; at 20 percent and 10 percent respectively, it is 16.7 cents per barrel.[17] As for operating costs, it is expected that "the efficiency of a drilling crew is reduced to about half that expected in California or Texas oil fields." [18] If so, the efficiency of current producing operations ought to be better than half, since they will be working under permanent living and working conditions. This is much like the Middle East and Libya where operating costs are around 6 cents.[19] Allowing the same range of variation for operating cost makes it 6 to 9 cents.

Then the lower range of Prudhoe Bay cost is 18 cents per barrel and the upper is 26 cents. Since the estimating formula is simple, anyone with access to better information can use it to get a better estimate. But even gross corrections would not make a very great deal of difference in absolute amounts.

FINDING COST AND RISK

One does what he can with relevant data, however fragmentary and imperfect, in order to explain and predict.[20] *The very low development-production cost is the only explanation for the headlong rush into the North Slope.* The companies do not want oil for oil's sake; there is more in the lower forty-eight than they will ever use; what they want is cheap oil. Very cheap oil found in one place is reason for hope elsewhere. The chapter on economic models [21] of petroleum exploration gives us the correct theory, into which there are as yet no numbers to be fitted. So far, there is no basis for estimating finding costs per barrel on the North Slope.[22] Nor do we need to know them; we are past that stage because we already know that there will be a big exploration effort. Big supplies available at low development cost will mean an important supply shift and price effect; small supplies or high development cost mean little change. As for lease payments, they are an effect of expected low development cost, a sharing of the expected profit. They are not a cost, and have no effect on price.

It matters much to the companies, but not to the analyst of supply shifts, that some operators will pay a bonus for a disappointment. Some will drill only dry holes. They will be luckier than those who find some marginal reservoir and throw good money after bad. Some may end up doing as well as or better than the companies developing the pool or pools around Prudhoe Bay. This dispersion of probabilities is what is meant by exploration risk: the chance of finding a given amount of oil of a given cheapness to develop, not of "finding oil." If the same amount of oil-in-place were indicated around Prudhoe Bay, but in such tight sands that extracting it would cost not 18-26 cents but five to ten times that much, there would be only mild interest in Alaska today. The mere presence of oil has been known for the better part of a century.

The odds against finding oil of a given cheapness are not the only kind of risk oil companies face. They must forecast prices over the life of whatever pools they hope to find, and how much of the price-cost difference will be taken by Alaska and by the federal government. The price will be a multiple of Prudhoe Bay development cost, but not necessarily of theirs. A company will reckon as best it can, then when it finds a field will conscientiously refigure, only to find that development cost is a bit higher, prices a bit lower, taxes a bit heavier—so that it would have been better off never having gone to the North Slope in the first place.

With all these factors to consider, there are two not to be considered. One is "replacement cost," which Lovejoy and Homan said over six years ago "has nothing in common with the concept of economic cost." [23]

The other irrelevance is in the thousands of wells drilled all over the world—which have no bearing on the odds of a find in Alaska. Indeed, we can make a stronger statement. During the ten years that ended in 1968, about 65,000 new-field wildcats were drilled in the United States. There will eventually be only 7 to 10 billion barrels of proved reserves developed from them, if prices and costs do not change too much. [24] If this record had even a remote bearing on Alaska prospects, then Alaska would be a good place to stay away from.

Oil finding in a new province is a high-risk business. Unsound arguments and irrelevant statistics offered on behalf of a sound thesis should not, but may, discredit it, harming not only oilmen.

ALASKAN OIL IN COMPETITION WITH OTHER AREAS

So much for history, and for the difficulties of prediction. To consider the chances of Alaskan oil in competition with other sources of supply in various markets we need first to take account of transport cost. Since the cost of traversing the Northwest Passage is unknown, the possibility must be disregarded.

Adding 22 cents production cost and 45 cents pipeline cost to Southern Alaskan tidewater,[25] from Valdez to Philadelphia, via Panama—about 9,000 nautical miles—crude oil could go in 240,000-ton tankers at approximately 35 cents [worldscale 40] plus less than 10 cents pipelining across Panama. Of course, if the Jones Act is applicable, the cost is double or more. Curiously enough, a Valdez–Puget Sound tanker run would cost about 8 cents and a transcontinental pipeline about 25 cents, the same total (within the margin for error). But since the Jones Act "penalty" would be much greater on the longer trip, it would seem to be out of the question if that Act governs—aside from the quota status of the oil. The point is that the real economic cost of laying down Prudhoe Bay crude on the East Coast is around $1.12 per barrel. Everything else is profit, including that part taken by Alaska, or by large-scale economic waste, a tribute to the Jones Act.

As for the Middle East, let us take Kuwait as a standard of comparison. Kuwait costs are about 10 cents, taxes about 85 cents, and freight to Japan 29 cents, so that the floor to prices under current conditions is $1.23. Prudhoe Bay oil would cost about 85 cents to lay down in Japan (20 + 45 + 20), leaving about 38 cents for development profits including taxes.

But this is no prediction that Prudhoe Bay oil or other Alaskan oil will actually go to any of those markets. For there is no public knowledge of what the limits of the field may be, and no hint of what future discoveries may contain. Let us make the extreme assumption that Prudhoe Bay development builds up to 2 million barrels daily, and then declines at a normal rate; while *no more* low-cost oil is found. If so, Alaskan oil probably will never go anywhere but to the West Coast. Suppose now that twice that capacity can be developed in this and other fields, at wellhead costs which are no more than twice (say 45 cents) as much for the last most expensive increment. If so, Alaskan oil can profitably undersell not "domestic U.S. oil" in general—which is meaningless—but enough of it so that if unhampered by restrictions on market forces, it will be delivered to the mid-continent and the East Coast even if the Northwest Passage cannot be traversed at a low enough cost. It all depends on how much it costs to develop a given capacity—price serves as the cut-off. Our calculations will be redone many times in the future.

In addition to discoveries, and to development and transport costs, one will need to consider Alaskan taxes. It will make a difference whether they are in cents per barrel; or percentages of price, or of gross or net income; and what the precise numbers will be. It will also make a difference whether Alaska goes beyond compulsory unitization and restrains output by market-demand-prorationing. There will be great pressure exerted and perhaps inducements offered to join the club, hold back output, and hold the price line. The Alaska Division of Oil and Gas seems to expect market-demand-prorationing, "in the light of industry prediction that production from the Arctic Slope may exceed two million barrels of oil per day by 1980," [26] and it may reach that figure much sooner.

Even if there were plenty of low-cost oil it might not be possible to sell it to Japan unless the price were considerably lower than it will be initially. What happens to price is hard to predict, but the pressure of Alaskan oil will tend to lower prices in the United States. The greater the discoveries the greater the pressure, but also the greater the political resistance. As always, the problem of inter-area shifts in oil supplies is one of more or less, not yes or no. There is still plenty of U.S. oil-in-place which can be developed into proved reserves and produced, at a cost which with allowance for transport cost can compete with Alaskan. Competition from Alaskan oil will tend to undermine the pro-rationing system in the big producing states of the lower forty-eight, thereby lowering costs there very appreciably. This would in turn tend to lower restrictions on imports. The lower U.S. prices go, the less the reason to maintain import controls. If at the extreme they became superfluous to security,[27] and were abolished, and U.S. crude oil prices joined the world structure, sales could be made to Japan at nondiscriminatory prices, and Alaskan oil could go there in large amounts while African–Persian Gulf crude went to the U.S. East Coast.

CONCLUSION

The only thing permanent in the world oil picture is change. New conditions enter as new information, in imperfectly known fragments. We need a supercomputer to digest the bits of data, make appropriate response, and then correct the many inevitable errors. Such an instument is available: a competitive price-profit system. In the socialist countries where it was formally abolished, it is now most badly missed. In the U.S. domestic oil industry, it was overlaid with so many controls over so many years that its essential principles are largely forgotten. This was no great matter as long as the controls could be maintained, but the pressures against them are accumulating. Even before Prudhoe Bay, Alaska never fitted into the U.S. industry too well, if only because output per well per day was 1,000 barrels as against the national average of 15. Perhaps in the 1970's Prudhoe Bay and neighboring fields will be, not the last straw, but the last ton. If so, thinking both in industry and government needs to be much more flexible than it has been up to now. The combination of protected U.S. prices plus big-oil costs is part of a mechanism whereby oil supply sources shift; but the mechanism has a feedback effect upon price. The Persian Gulf price is today about a third of what it was just after World War II, despite the rise in the general price level; and it is still going down. Alaskan oil will in some way fit into the picture, and too great a resistance to the forces of change only increases the damage. If the state and the oil companies, together or separately, reach for more than can be got, they will receive less.

NOTES

1. Similar data are not available for natural gas liquids. Hence these numbers are not strictly comparable with Table 1.
2. API-AGA, *Reserves of Crude Oil, Natural Gas Liquids, and Natural Gas in the United States and Canada* (1968), p. 15.
3. Let q_t be the current output of a well, q_a be the "economic limit" or output just prior to abandonment, and a be the decline rate. Then proved reserves are $\int t = a \ q_t e^{-at} \ dt$.
4. And also from forecasts of what new oil-in-place will be discovered, which have no bearing on the problems discussed here.
5. John D. Moody, address to the Southwestern section of the AAPG, February 7, 1968 (mimeographed).
6. M. A. Adelman, "Trends in the Cost of Finding and Developing Oil and Gas Reserves," in Gardner and Hanke, *Essays in Petroleum Economics* (University of Colorado Press, 1967). See also National Petroleum Council, *Impact of New Technology on the U.S. Petroleum Industry, 1946–1965* (1967), Part 1, especially Chapters 2-4.
7. API-AGA, *op. cit.,* pp. 29, 128, 275.

8. M. A. Adelman, "Oil Production Costs in Four Areas," *Proceedings of the Council on Economics of the American Institute of Mining, Metallurgical, and Petroleum Engineers (AIME) 1966.* The calculations made there have been extensively revised and should no longer be quoted. The paper is a chapter in *The World Petroleum Market* (in press).

9. *Oil & Gas Journal,* August 11, 1969, pp. 105-137.

10. Atlantic Richfield, *Annual Report 1968,* p. 12.

11. *Joint Association Survey 1967,* Tables 11-14.

12. *Oil & Gas Journal, op. cit.*

13. In an earlier draft, this cost was considered as part of the miscellaneous chance factors to be covered by higher than necessary costs of capital.

14. See Bob T. H. Hulsey, "Rate of Return—an Investment Tool," in vol. 2 of *Exploration and Economics of the Petroleum Industry* (Houston: Gulf Publishing Company, 1964), p. 22; and references cited in "Oil Production Costs," *op. cit.*

15. For example, there is the cost of equipping the lease, i.e., the group of wells whose production is rid of gas and of basic sand and water, stored, and run to the pipeline. (Fluid injection is excluded because it would lower the decline rate and reduce costs.) Data are sparse, and U.S. figures not relevant though the item is very small by comparison with drilling cost.

16. *(a)* Assume 75-25 debt-equity, and that about one-sixth of net income is paid in Federal income taxes, then 18 percent before taxes is needed for 15 percent after. The net pre-tax return is (.75 × 18) + (.25 × 7.5), or 15.38, rounded to 15 percent.

   (b) This is an underestimate of profit after tax, because of the effect of current expensing of intangibles. If $218 is spent per daily barrel, and two-thirds is currently expensed, then $137 per year is deductible from taxable income, or 38 cents per barrel. Therefore if current operating cost is 6 cents (see below), and price is as high as 44 cents, no tax is payable. This would provide a much higher rate of return, both pre- and post-tax. Were drilling to proceed at a steady rate, as the company found new reservoirs, no tax would be due at any time in respect of North Slope operations, and at least there will be none in the early years. But we cannot tell how long this will go on. Hence I prefer to leave current expensing as a reinforcement to the main point, that if the minimum necessary cost of equity capital is 15 percent after tax, our allowance of 15 percent before tax on the total investment is more than sufficient.

   (c) Alternatively, we might reckon that with price (see below) at:

	17.5 cents	*25.7 cents*
1. Annual gross profit per daily barrel	$64.00	$94.00
2. Less interest at 7.5 percent	3.75	3.75
3. Less depletion at 20 percent gross revenues, assuming change from current 27.5 percent.	12.80	18.80
4. Taxable income (1-2-3)	47.45	72.55
5. Tax	23.72	36.28
6. Profit after tax (1-2-5)	36.53	40.03
7. Percent of equity	22.3	23.5

17. Unit capital cost is equal to $218/(365 × 5.18), *or* to $218/ (365 × 3.59), where 5.18 and 3.59 are the respective present values of an annuity declining at 5 or at 10 percent, discounted at 15 or at 20 percent. The respective Present-Barrels-Equivalent (PBE) are 1,890 and 1,220. "Oil Production Costs," *op. cit.*

18. Atlantic Richfield, *Annual Report 1968,* p. 12.

19. See *The World Petroleum Market, op. cit.,* Chapter 2.

20. Perhaps I may be permitted to recall two earlier attempts with data no better: a prediction in 1963 that world oil prices would decline, not rise, and in 1964 that residual fuel oil at the U.S. East Coast would, if decontrolled, decline from over $2 per barrel to $1.50. The current Boston price is between $1.60 and $1.65. (See "Oil Prices in the Long Run," *Journal of Business of the University of Chicago,* April 1964, and "Heavy Fuel Oil Supply and Price," November 20, 1964 (mimeographed, published as "L'Offre et le Prix du Fuel aux USA," *Revue Française de l'Energie,* June 1965). [The drashe rise in 1970, in consequence of the tanker shortage, will soon be reversed.]

21. See the chapter by Paul G. Bradley, "Exploration Models and Petroleum Production Economics," p. 93 in this text.

22. The method of Maximum Economic Finding Cost (MEFC) suggested in "Oil Production Costs in Four Areas," *op. cit.,* is not applicable here.

23. Wallace F. Lovejoy and Paul T. Homan, *Cost Analysis in the Petroleum Industry* (Dallas: Southern Methodist University Press, 1963), p. 17; and earlier discussions cited there.

24. Fred A. Dix, Jr., and L. H. Van Dyke, "North American Drilling Activity in 1968," AAPG *Bulletin,* June 1969.

25. A pipeline carrying 2 million barrels daily is expected to cost about $1.5 billion. We assume it will take five years to build the line and work up to maximum capacity, while in fact more than half is expected to be operating by 1972; and that the cost of capital, at 85 percent debt and 15 percent equity, is 10 percent. Then the funds committed by the end of the fifth year may be reckoned with some exaggeration as worth $0.3 Σ $(1.1)^5$ = $2.1 billion. There is no decline rate, so the integral calculated by the method of note 17 is 10.0, and the cost per barrel is 29 cents. Operating costs would normally be 5-7 cents; the unusual terrain may put it as high as 15 cents. Total pipelining then comes to 45 cents in round figures. This is on the high side.

26. See *Oil & Gas Compact Bulletin,* vol. 28, June 1969, p. 32.

27. My opinion, stated most recently before the Hart Subcommittee of the U.S. Senate in March 1969, is that import controls are needed for national security. But this is no support for any particular method, let alone the present system. Moreover, the need may pass in time.

Economic Analysis of
Prudhoe Bay Oil Field

*Charles A. Norman**

INTRODUCTION

The North Slope of Alaska (the area between the Brooks Range and the Arctic Ocean) has long been recognized as part of a potentially large oil-producing basin. In 1923, after oil seeps were discovered at Cape Simpson, a major portion of the North Slope was designated a Naval Petroleum Reserve by presidential order. During the period from 1944 to 1953, the federal government conducted exploratory work including the drilling of 36 wildcat wells and 44 core holes. After spending an estimated $51 million in the nine-year effort the government had made three oil and gas discoveries, one of which, Umiat oil field, is estimated to contain from 30 million to 100 million barrels of recoverable reserves; the other two fields were both small. A field with reserves of 100 million barrels is a major discovery in the lower southern forty-eight," but Umiat was considered too small to be a commercial field in the Territory of Alaska in 1953.

In 1957 commerical oil production was established in

* Charles A. Norman is Division Manager of Exploration of the Continental Oil Company, Denver, Colorado.

31

southern Alaska on the Kenai Peninsula. The rush to explore Alaska's sedimentary basins was on, and the North
Slope was opened for public leasing in 1958. In the decade
between 1958 and 1968, American companies conducted
geological and geophysical surveys and drilled a long string
of exploratory wells without a commercial discovery. Then
on April 22, 1967, Atlantic Richfield, as operator in a joint
venture with Humble Oil and Refining Company (sub-
sidiary of Standard Oil of New Jersey), spudded in the Prudhoe Bay State No. 1 well, just two miles from the shore of
the Arctic Ocean on a 90,000-acre block of state leases.

On February 16, 1968, Atlantic Richfield announced that
the Prudhoe Bay State No. 1 well had encountered both oil
and gas. The zones were in a Triassic sand body 470 feet
thick, the base of which was encountered at 8,708 feet.
Atlantic Richfield and its partner, Humble Oil and Refining
Company, then drilled a second well seven miles southeast
of the Prudhoe Bay State No. 1. On June 25, 1968, Atlantic
Richfield announced that the second well, named the Sag
River State No. 1, had encountered oil in the same Triassic
formations as the initial well. Atlantic Richfield announced
at this time that on a production test the Prudhoe Bay State
No. 1 had flowed oil at various rates up to 2,415 barrels of
30.5 degree API gravity oil per day.

Atlantic Richfield then retained the services of DeGolyer
and MacNaughton, one of the most respected consulting
engineering firms in the industry, to evaluate the discovery
based on geophysical mapping and the results of the two
wells. On July 18, 1968, Atlantic Richfield's chairman, Robert O. Anderson, quoted from the DeGolyer and Mac-
Naughton report:

> In our opinion this important discovery could de-
> velop into a field with recoverable reserves of some five
> to ten billion barrels of oil, which would rate as one of
> the largest petroleum accumulations known to the world
> today. The major part of the field appears to lie on a

90,000-acre block of leases in which Atlantic Richfield Company and Humble Oil and Refining Company each owns a 50 percent working interest. Two wells have been drilled to date on the block.

Anderson also announced at that time that the Sag River State No. 1 had encountered 300 feet of oil sand in the same Triassic formation found in the first well and that the Sag River well had flowed oil at the rate of 2,300 barrels a day.

Significance of Size—Prudhoe Bay Field

If the actual reserves of Prudhoe Bay field turn out to be in the upper range of DeGolyer and MacNaughton's 5-billion- to 10-billion-barrel estimate, it will be the largest field ever found in North America. The present champion is East Texas field, discovered in 1930, with an expected ultimate production of 6 billion barrels. The proved reserves of the United States before the Prudhoe Bay discovery were estimated at between 35 and 40 billion barrels. So in the summer of 1968, shortly after the discovery, it appeared probable that the new field would increase the proved reserves of the United States from 15 to 25 percent. If any doubts existed as to how the industry sized up the discovery, they were quickly dispelled on September 10, 1969, when the state of Alaska added over $900 million to its treasury from winning bids for state oil and gas leases on the North Slope. Since the September lease sale no one has been talking about Prudhoe Bay field in terms of 5 billion barrels—it's almost always referred to now as a 10-billion-barrel field. The clincher for the larger estimate was added shortly after the sale, when British Petroleum released a report by DeGolyer and MacNaughton which estimated British Petroleum's reserves in the field to be 4.8 billion barrels.

Another measure of the tremendous size of Prudhoe Bay

field is gained from a comparison of its expected average daily production with the production from the world's largest fields. Most oil industry leaders expect that Prudhoe Bay field will reach a peak production of at least 1 million barrels per day. The operators of the field have stated that the pipeline from the North Slope will probably be expanded to eventually carry 2 million barrels a day, so the 1 million barrels per day is probably the minimum figure. For the first six months of 1968, only two fields in the Western countries (individual field statistics are unavailable from the Soviet Union) averaged over 1 million barrels per day. Saudi Arabia's Ghawar field averaged 1.53 million barrels per day, and Burgan field in Kuwait probably produced 2 million barrels per day of Kuwait's 2.25 million barrels per day (Kuwait's production is not available by field). These comparisons are made only to point out that the state of Alaska stands a very good chance of having the world's number-one producing oil field by the late 1970's.

Problems of Development

The Alaskan North Slope presents engineering problems which are formidable to say the least. The North Slope is a low-relief, treeless plain dotted with lakes and streams and covered with tundra. The tundra, 12 inches to a few feet thick, is a surface layer consisting of soil, moss, and lichens; and it freezes concrete-hard in winter and thaws to a spongy, clumped prairie land in summer. No roads traverse the tundra. In summer man moves by airplane, helicopter, or foot. In winter the Arctic equivalent of the truck convoy appears—the "cat train." Tractor-drawn, skid-mounted cargo carriers roll in long columns across the frozen surface, some coming from as far away as Fairbanks, 390 miles to the south.

Below the tundra is the permafrost, that part of the subsoil which remains permanently frozen. On parts of the

North Slope the permafrost extends more than 1,000 feet below the surface. One veteran engineer with experience on the North Slope explained one of the problems associated with the permafrost as follows:

> Two steel pilings on display at the University of Alaska at Fairbanks testify to the toughness of permafrost. Both crumpled like soda straws when pile drivers attempted to pound them down. Most piling holes in the Arctic are drilled with augers. Normal ditch-digging machinery penetrates the permafrost about as fast as it would regular concrete.

Although the permafrost is a formidable barrier to penetration, it represents a larger problem when it is artificially melted. In the summer months, when the tundra thaws, it acts as an insulating layer for the underlying permafrost. If the tundra is removed the permafrost melts, and the released water becomes a potentially active agent of erosion. An incident that happened at Barrow illustrates the problems connected with melting permafrost. To provide drainage of water from an asphalt plant during airstrip paving operations, a small ditch—18 by 18 inches—was dug several hundred feet to the edge of the Arctic Ocean. The tundra had been stripped off, warm temperatures began to melt the permafrost, and the drainage water moved briskly along the ditch. In six weeks the ditch was six feet deep and eight to ten feet wide. Because of problems such as this, buildings in the Arctic are put on pilings to allow sufficient "cold space" above the tundra, or they are built on gravel pads three to four feet high. The gravel serves to insulate the ground from the building heat. It is possible that all crude oil pipelines will have to be laid on or within a gravel pad on top of the tundra to prevent the heat flow from melting the underlying permafrost. Any oil storage tank will have to be built on a foundation which insulates the ground from the heat of the tank. All building foundations, drilling locations, and roads will probably be built on gravel pads three to four feet thick. Fortunately for the oil operators a large supply of gravel exists in the bed of the Sagavanirktok River, which is adjacent to the Sag River State No. 1 well.

There is one problem connected with permafrost, however, which cannot be solved by insulation with gravel. That is the problem of the permafrost's being melted adjacent to the well casing as the hot oil flows from 8,500 feet deep in the earth up to the surface. As this happens the surface of the ground will probably subside in the vicinity of the well, creating engineering problems with both the well casing and surface installations. Although these problems may require major engineering accomplishments, the industry bids at the state lease sale seemed to say that these major engineering ills can be cured with minor economic medicine.

Transportation of Crude to Market

Assuming that Prudhoe Bay oil can be efficiently produced, the operators will still face the task of economically transporting it to market. Of the many possible methods of transport to market, three methods are receiving the most attention:

1. An 800-mile pipeline from Prudhoe Bay to the southern coast of Alaska at the port of Valdez, then by tanker to other United States ports, and possibly Japan.

2. A 1,500-mile pipeline across Canada to Edmonton, Alberta, where it would connect with existing pipelines or additional lines to take crude into the Chicago and Toledo areas.

3. Direct transport from Prudhoe Bay by supertankers fitted with special ice-breaking equipment which would enable them to operate year round in the Arctic Ocean. This

concept was tested by the S.S. *Manhattan* when it negotiated the Northwest Passage in the late summer of 1969, went on to Prudhoe Bay, and returned to New York in November.

The foregoing perhaps will serve as a useful background for those not familiar with Prudhoe Bay field. The primary objective of this study, however, is to determine the cost of placing Prudhoe Bay crude oil in various world markets. This means the cost of production plus the cost of transportation. The cost of production is defined as the lowest price at which the oil could be sold at the wellhead and still provide the required rate of return to all capital investments over the life of the project. Likewise, the cost of transportation is defined as the lowest transportation charge that could be made for the oil that would provide the required rate of return for all capital investments over the life of the project. Or stated another way, the cost of producing the oil is the price at which the oil could be sold at the wellhead in order to just break even over the life of the project when all future cash flows are discounted at the cost of capital.

A cautionary note needs to be added to emphasize what the cost of production does not include. The cost of production of oil as defined here does not include any costs of exploration or lease acquisitions. On a time scale, all costs incurred before the drilling of a discovery well of a field are excluded from the cost of production, while all costs associated with the discovery well and all production costs thereafter are included in the cost of production.

FINANCIAL ASPECTS

Of prime importance in the evaluation of any capital investment is the cost of capital. Because the cost of capital is largely determined by the investing public, let us digress briefly in order to see how that investing public and analysts of brokerage firms evaluated the discovery of Prudhoe Bay field shortly after its discovery.

Stock market investors were quick to react to every piece of encouraging news concerning the Atlantic Richfield Prudhoe Bay State No. 1 and Sag River State No. 1 wells. From January 16, 1968, when Atlantic Richfield announced a good gas test in the Prudhoe State No. 1, until the fall of 1968 after the existence of the super-giant oil field had been well publicized, the common stock of Atlantic Richfield rose in price from 53 1/8 to a high of 130 1/4 on November 29, 1968. (All prices and volumes of Atlantic Richfield's common stock have been adjusted to reflect the 2 for 1 stock split of August, 1968.)

It is interesting to note the reaction of the stock market to Robert O. Anderson's announcement of the DeGolyer and MacNaughton report, which estimated the size of the field at 5 to 10 billion barrels. Anderson's announcement was made on Thurday morning, July 18, 1968, before the New York Stock Exchange opened for trading. Because of the tremendous influx of "buy" orders which followed Anderson's announcement, Atlantic Richfield's common and convertible preferred stocks did not open for trading on the New York Stock Exchange that day. However, the common stock of Standard Oil Company (New Jersey) was up 2 3/4 for the day, representing an increase in the market value of the firm's 215 million common shares of over $591 million. The next day the stock price of Jersey Standard jumped 2 1/8 points more for an additional stock valuation increase of $456 million.

Atlantic Richfield stock did not open for trading Friday either, nor did it open for trading Monday morning. At 1:48 P.M. on Monday, July 22, the common stock traded on a block of 120,000 shares at 91, up 17 1/4 from the previous Tuesday's close (the New York Stock Exchange was closed on the Wednesday prior to Anderson's announcement). It eventually closed Monday at 88 1/2, up 14 3/4 for the day on a total volume of 202,000 shares. The Atlantic Richfield $3 convertible preferred stock closed at 148 1/2, up 23 7/8 for the day on volume of 36,500 shares. The increase in market price of the two classes of stock was over $571 million for the day. This stock price seems all the more spectacular on realizing that it occurred on a day when the stock market in general was extremely weak, with 1,105 issues declining and only 264 advancing. The Dow Jones Industrial Average was down 13.60 points, its biggest loss in over a year.

The combined rise in the market value of the stocks of the two companies on the first day that each was traded after Anderson's July 18 announcement totaled $1.162 billion. As a first approximation, this figure might be taken as the value that the investing public placed on the field in the summer of 1968. Before anyone seriously considers using a value of $1.16 billion for the field, however, he should temper its usefulness by comparing the price action of the common stocks of the two companies. For the month of trading following the July 18 announcement, the stock of Jersey Standard remained in a fairly narrow range centered around the price of 77 1/8 at which it closed trading the day of the announcement, and at the end of the year the stock closed at 78 5/8. On the other hand, Atlantic Richfield's stock climbed quite steadily from the price of 88 1/2 at which it closed on the day it resumed trading after the announcement. By the end of the year the stock was priced at 118 after having reached a peak of 130 1/4.

This, of course, does not mean to imply that the stock price action of the two companies for the last half of 1968 was due entirely to the discovery of Prudhoe Bay field. The suggestion made here is that in the first few weeks following the "5- to 10-billion-barrel" announcement, investors seemed to be evaluating Jersey Standard's 50 percent interest in the field as worth at least $500 million, and Atlantic Richfield's 50 percent interest as worth at least $750 million. There are a number of reasons why a $250 million difference would arise in evaluating the two companies' interest in the field. There are logical reasons why a given amount of crude oil in Alaska would indeed be more valuable to Atlantic Richfield than to Jersey Standard. It is quite easy to imagine that large production on the North Slope could cause a decrease in profits for Jersey Standard in other areas—notably in Venezuela. Atlantic Richfield, on the other hand, could probably benefit the most by maximizing profits from North Slope oil. There is also the point that stock market speculators who were convinced of the great value of the Prudhoe Bay discovery would naturally pick the company in which the field represented the largest percentage of total company value, thereby diminishing the effect of other corporate business on the rise in stock price.

In the foregoing, any reference to the stock market response to British Petroleum's share of the field has intentionally been omitted. Even though it now appears that British Petroleum has at least as large a share of the field as either one of the discovering partners, in those first weeks following the discovery British Petroleum's position in the field was poorly defined, and no definitive announcement was made by the company until after it had drilled its first well.

COST OF EQUITY CAPITAL

The practice of discounting future cash flows, at what is termed the "appropriate rate," seems to be universally accepted by authors of economic analyses. The question, however, of what the "appropriate rate" is for different kinds of investments is often avoided by using the statement that "this figure varies depending on the financial structure of the individual company." Davis has stated that the investor's rate of return earned by the producing industry is probably between 8 and 16 percent, but he gives no reasons for using this range.[1] He defines investor's rate of return as the maximum interest rate at which funds could be borrowed to finance a project such that the project will just break even. A favorite of many authors in the past for the cost of capital was 10 percent. In recent years, however, with interest rates on the rise, the most common figure seems to be 15 percent for the oil-producing industry. For purposes of this paper, the value that is needed is the after-tax cost of capital, which includes the cost of equity capital and debt capital, weighted in accordance with their respective shares of a firm's capital structure. An attempt to measure the cost of equity capital will be made by examining three different methods.

Gordon-Shapiro Method

Gordon and Shapiro have used the "dividend valuation model" to determine a firm's cost of equity capital.[2] The general form of the equation is

$$k_e = \frac{D}{P} + g$$

where k_e = the rate of return demanded by investors for equity capital in the firm, D = dividends per share, P = price per share of the stock, and g = expected growth rate of dividends. Gordon and Shapiro argue that the lower limit for rate of profit on any asset of a company should be the rate of profit that shareholders expect from owning a share of the company's stock. The rate of profit from owning a share of stock is dependent on the current dividend yield plus the future growth of dividends. They arrive at a determination of future dividends by means of two assumptions. One, a corporation is expected to retain a fraction of its income after taxes; and two, a corporation is expected to earn a return on the book value of its common equity, which is dependent on the amount of the corporation's retained earnings. They define k as the "growth rate of profit," which can be written as

$$k = \frac{D}{P} + \frac{Y - D}{B}$$

where D = dividends, P = price of stock, Y = earnings, and B = book value; all values are per share of common stock. That is, they are saying that

$$g = \frac{Y - D}{B}$$

Gordon and Shapiro's method is easy to apply in practice because all factors of the equation for determining k are available for most corporations. One problem arises, however, because of the time lag involved in reporting book value and earnings. The investing public is buying and selling a corporation's shares without knowing up-to-date values of earnings and especially book value. For example, although an individual investor knows the current price of a stock, he is usually between one and thirteen months out-of-date on the book value of that stock. This fact suggests that the best time for computing k may be on the date of issue of the annual financial statement of a corporation. However, without attempting to justify the reasons for it, I have arbitrarily elected to test Gordon and Shapiro's formula by taking stock prices during a given year and the other values as of the end of that year.

In Table 3, k has been computed for Standard Oil Company (New Jersey) for the years 1959 to 1968. Two values of k are given, one for the highest stock price of the year and one for the lowest. In the past 10 years, the lowest value of k was 5.9 percent during 1959 when the stock sold at a price-earnings ratio of 20 to 1. The highest k value was 10.4 percent during 1968 when the price-earnings ratio fell to 11 to 1. In all three cases where a value of k was reached exceeding 10 percent, k was based on a stock price which

Table 3

Cost of Equity Capital from Gordon-Shapiro Method
Jersey Standard

Year	Price Range			Divi-dend	Earn-ings	Book Value	k at Highest Price	k at Lowest Price
	High	Low	Last					
1968	85⅛	66⅝	78⅝	$3.65	$5.93*	$45.62	.093	.105
1967	70⅝	59⅜	67½	3.45	5.37*	44.15	.092	.101
1966	84¼	59¾	63⅛	3.30	5.06	41.92	.081	.097
1965	90⅜	73⅝	80⅜	3.15	4.74	39.89	.075	.083
1964	92⅞	75	90⅛	3.00	4.87	38.74	.081	.088
1963	76⅝	58⅜	76	2.75	4.74	37.04	.090	.101
1962	59¾	45⅜	59½	2.50	3.88	35.39	.081	.094
1961	52	40¾	50¾	2.30	3.50	33.00	.081	.093
1960	50½	38	41¼	2.25	3.18	31.72	.074	.089
1959	59¼	45⅝	49⅝	2.25	2.91	31.17	.059	.071

$$k = \frac{D}{P} + \frac{Y-D}{B}$$

* Accounting changes in 1968 resulted in a downward adjustment of 1967 earnings to $5.37/share from $5.54. These changes had the effect of lowering 1968 earnings to $5.93 from $6.07.

occurred very early in the calendar year—approximately one full year before the earnings and book value on which k also depended were known. The values for 1967 and 1968 suggest that investors in Standard Oil Company (New Jersey) have recently been expecting a profit after taxes of about 10 percent per year (where the growth of expected future dividends is taken account of).

A similar application of the Gordon-Shapiro method was made to Atlantic Richfield. The results, however, were at best confusing and at worst completely useless. The trouble is centered in accounting practices which were employed to adjust the book value *(B)* of Atlantic Richfield stock after two large mergers. The first was after the merger of Richfield Oil Company with Atlantic Refining Company, when the book value went from $32.28 per share for Atlantic Refining Company in 1964 to $17.15 per share for Atlantic Richfield Company in 1965 after the merger.

The second large change in book value was from 1967 to
1968 when it dropped from $19.87 per share to $15.07 per
share after the merger of Sinclair into Atlantic Richfield.

The Gordon-Shapiro equation indicates that investors
require a rate of return of 9 or 10 percent for Standard Oil
Company (New Jersey). The values obtained from the Gordon-Shapiro equation, however, can only be used as approximations for the two subject companies because the
equation represents a special case. As Miller and Modigliani have pointed out, the Gordon-Shapiro equation is
applicable only to the special case where the firm uses no
external sources of financing.[3] I have used the Gordon-
Shapiro method here mainly to serve as a comparison for
other methods of measurement.

Past Rate of Growth as a Measure of "g"

Many authors have suggested that a company's expected
growth rate of dividends can best be estimated by using its
historical growth rate. Miller and Modigliani, in determining investment opportunities of a firm, use a linear five-
year average growth rate of total assets. However, for
showing growth over a period of years, I prefer to use the
compounded growth rate of earnings, that is, the rate of
which the earnings in any past year would have had to
grow, compounded annually, in order to equal the present
earnings. Table 4 shows the growth rate of earnings through
1968 for Atlantic Richfield and Jersey Standard by using the years 1963 through 1967 as different base years.
Therefore the most recent five-, four-, three,- two-, and one-
year growth rates are shown. Also shown are the simple
annual percentage increases in earnings for each year from
1964 through 1968.

The problem that now presents itself is which historical
period should be used as representative of a company's
present and future growth rate. The two companies under

Table 4

Growth Rate of Earnings
Standard Oil Company (New Jersey)

	1963	1964	1965	1966	1967	1968
Earnings Per Share	$4.74	$4.87	$4.74	$5.06	$5.37	$5.93
Percentage Increase from Previous Year	22.2	2.7	−2.7	6.8	6.1	10.4
Period	1963-1968	1964-1968	1965-1968	1966-1968	1967-1968	
% Growth Rate of Earnings	4.6	5.0	7.8	8.3	10.4	

Growth Rate of Earnings
Atlantic Richfield Company

	1963	1964	1965	1966	1967	1968
Earnings Per Share	$2.19	$2.35	$2.74	$3.61	$4.28	$4.78
Percentage Increase from Previous Year	−8.0	7.3	16.6	31.7	18.5	11.7
Period	1963-1968	1964-1968	1965-1968	1966-1968	1967-1968	
% Growth Rate of Earnings	16.9	19.4	20.4	15.1	11.7	

consideration show very different growth rate trends for the last part of the five-year period. While Jersey Standard has shown a favorable increase in its growth rate over the past three years, Atlantic Richfield's rate of earnings growth has turned down for the past two years. It seems likely that the extremely high growth rate of Atlantic Richfield from 1963 to 1967 was significantly greater than its long-term trend.

Because it is felt that the most recent earnings report is, by far, the most important one for predicting future earnings, I have used a simple weighted average of past growth to predict the short-term growth rate. In this weighted historical average, the most recent year's percentage increase in earnings (1968 vs. 1967) is given twice the weight of the percentage change that occurred the year before (1967 vs.

1966). Likewise the 1967 vs. 1966 change is weighted twice as heavily as the 1966 vs. 1965 change. For the sake of simplicity in calculating the sum of this infinite series, all values more than six years in the past have been dropped. The calculations for the two companies are shown in Table 5.

Table 5

Weighted Historical Average Growth Rate
Jersey Standard

Year	% Earnings Change	Weight	Product (2x3)
1968 vs. 1967	10.4	32	332.8
1967 vs. 1966	6.1	16	97.6
1966 vs. 1965	6.8	8	54.4
1965 vs. 1964	−2.7	4	−10.8
1964 vs. 1963	2.7	2	5.4
1963 vs. 1962	22.2	1	22.2
Total		63	501.6

$$\text{Weighted Historical Average of } g = \frac{501.6}{63} = 8.0\%$$

Weighted Historical Average Growth Rate
Atlantic Richfield

Year	% Earnings Change	Weight	Product (2x3)
1968 vs. 1967	11.7	32	374.4
1967 vs. 1966	18.5	16	296.0
1966 vs. 1965	31.7	8	253.6
1965 vs. 1964	16.6	4	66.4
1964 vs. 1963	7.3	2	14.6
1963 vs. 1962	−8.0	1	−8.0
Total		63	997.0

$$\text{Weighted Historical Average of } g = \frac{997}{63} = 15.8\%$$

In the weighted historical average, I have placed extremely heavy emphasis on the most recent years at the expense of the early years. This was intentional. As a matter of comparison, a weighting system placing more emphasis on earlier years did not change the resulting values greatly.

For example, a weighting system which weights the last six years' earnings changes in the ratios of 6-5-4-3-2-1 (from most recent to earliest) gives a value for g (growth rate of earnings) of 6.6 percent for Jersey Standard and 16.5 percent for Atlantic Richfield, compared with 8 per cent and 15.8 percent respectively for the weighted historical average.

The weighted historical average values of g are also consistent with the values that an "eyeball judgment" would reach based on the compounded growth rates from Table 5.

An interesting comparison can now be made between the weighted historical average value of g and the value of g derived using the Gordon-Shapiro method, $\dfrac{(Y-D)}{(B)}$. For Jersey Standard the weighted historical average is 8.0 percent versus a figure near 5 percent for the Gordon-Shapiro method.

The general equation of the dividend valuation model for the cost of equity capital can be solved using the weighted historical average. Using 1968 dividends and closing 1968 stock prices, the k_e for Jersey Standard is

$$k_e = \frac{D}{P} + g = \frac{3.65}{78.625} + .080 = .126 = 12.6\%$$

and for Atlantic Richfield

$$k_e = \frac{D}{P} + g = \frac{1.675}{118} + .158 = .172 = 17.2\%$$

Earnings Evaluation Model

A form of the earnings evaluation model has been used by Crowell to determine the cost of equity capital.[4] The primary basis of his determination of g is from predictions by security analysts. One of the groups of companies analyzed by Crowell consisted of 14 major integrated oil companies. Both Jersey Standard and Atlantic Richfield were members of the group. Crowell found that investors seemed to require a premium on the order of 4 to 7 percentage points above the long-term interest rate (as defined by new utility "A" bonds) for investing in oil equities during the period from mid-1964 to early 1967. The 4 percent figure generally applied from mid-1964 to mid-1966 and the 7 percent figure generally applied from mid-1966 to early 1967, the end of his period of study. By assuming that the premium over long-term interest rates required by investors in early 1969 is roughly the same as it was in early 1967, an average cost of equity capital for the group of 14 oil companies is inferred to be about 16 percent. Such a cost for equity capital is derived by adding the 7 percent premium to the current yield on "A" bonds of about 9 percent. This figure, of course, is the average value of all 14 companies in the group. Note that the 16 percent figure falls between the Jersey Standard (12.6%) and Atlantic Richfield (17.2%) figures derived from the dividend-valuation model using the weighted historical average value for *g*.

Value Used

Of the three foregoing methods of measuring the cost of equity capital, which should be used? Although the values derived from the Gordon-Shapiro equation serve as interesting comparisons, the author rejects their validity because the companies involved use large amounts of debt financing. The dividend-valuation model, using the weighted historical average for *g*, produces a rather wide range (12.6 percent to 17.2 percent) of results. Crowell's earnings-valuation model produces a range of values which is an average of 14 large oil companies; a range of values that appears to center around 16 percent. As a compromise figure between the weighted historical average and Crowell's values, a figure of 15 percent will be used in this paper for the cost of equity capital. An apology is herewith made to the "many authors" referred to a few pages previously who have been using 15 percent as the cost of equity capital for the past few years. My long-winded efforts may add a small bit of weight to the argument for using that figure.

The debt-to-equity ratio of major oil companies as shown on their balance sheets is usually an understatement of the true debt. This is because of large amounts of off-balance sheet debt in the form of long-term leases (chiefly for tankers and service stations). Moody's gives Jersey Standard's long-term debt as 13.7 percent of capitalization at the end of 1967, most of which was listed as subsidiaries' debt. The actual $1.5 billion listed as long-term debt would amount to 9.3 percent of the valuation of Jersey Standard if valuation is defined as stock price times number of shares plus book value of debt. No estimate of the amount of debt in the form of leases is available for Jersey Standard, but for purposes of comparison the author believes that it is not unreasonable to assume that its proportion of leases to balance sheet debt is roughly the same as for Texaco Incorporated.

Texaco Incorporated listed net lease payments (having longer than three years to run) due during 1968 as $96 million, which was 10.2 percent as large as its book value of long-term debt. The question that now arises is how long into the future should this figure be used as an annual average when some leases expire in three years and some in twenty-five years. The author also believes it is reasonable to assume that the total lease commitment of major oil companies is approximately ten times the current year's payments. This assumption would mean that Texaco has long-term lease commitments of about $960 million—an additional amount about equal to the book value of its stated long-term debt. If this condition also is true of Jersey Standard, and if leases are considered as simply more long-term debt, then debt plus leases was approximately 17 percent of the total valuation of Jersey Standard at the end of 1967 (where valuation is equal to stock price times shares plus book value of debt). Of course, the increase in interest rates during the past few years has substantially reduced the market value of most major oil companies' long-term debt, and total valuation should be based not only on market value of stock but on market value of debt also. If adjustment is made for increased interest rates the 17 percent figure for Jersey Standard would probably be reduced to about 15 percent.

In the case of Atlantic Richfield a much better estimate of the actual debt structure of the company can be made. In footnotes of its annual reports, the company lists the amount of long-term lease obligations outstanding at year-end. The amount of long-term lease obligations plus long-term debt was 17.4 percent of Atlantic Richfield's valuation at the end of 1967 (using the closing 1967 stock price). The large rise in stock price since the end of 1967 has, of course, caused a drastic cut in this percentage of debt for Atlantic Richfield. It seems reasonable to assume, however, that the company will take advantage of the stock price rise in order to issue new debt securities in the future.

A value of 16 percent of valuation for debt and long-term leases (or a debt to equity ratio of .19) for Atlantic Richfield and Jersey Standard will be used for our computations. The author feels that, if anything, this value is on the low side.

WEIGHTED AVERAGE COST OF CAPITAL

In order to determine the total cost of capital for developing Prudhoe Bay field, the weighted average cost of capital approach will be used, with the following assumptions:

1. Sixteen percent of capital investments in Prudhoe Bay field will come from debt financing, and 80 percent of capital investment for pipelines will come from debt financing.

2. The corporate income tax rate will average 50 percent over the next few years (with and without the surtax).

3. The long-term interest rate for oil companies' debt financing will be 9.0 percent for the next few years.

4. The cost of equity capital will be 15 percent for both new capital and retained earnings (flotation costs are ignored).

The weighted average cost of capital for developing Prudhoe Bay field, therefore, is given by:

(1) Method of Financing	(2) Proportion	(3) Cost after Taxes	(4) Weighted Cost (2x3)
Debt	.16	4.5%	0.7%
Equity	.84	15.0%	12.6%

Weighted Average Cost of Capital = 13.3%

The best value to use for discounting future cash flows associated with production from Prudhoe Bay field appears to be about 13.3 percent. In order to be on the conservative side (conservative in this case meaning to allow for unforeseen risks) a basic value of 15 percent will be used to discount cash flows associated with the field.

In discounting cash flows associated with investments in trunk pipeline systems, however, a slightly different approach will be used. Pipelines are traditionally built with very heavy debt financing so long as the pipeline is assured of having long-term contracts to transport oil. White uses a 10 percent/90 percent ratio of equity to debt financing as representative of large pipeline investments.[5] From communications with members of investment banking concerns, the author has been given the opinion that a trans-Alaskan pipeline could be financed 90 percent with debt money if the pipeline had a favorable through-put contract with operators of Prudhoe Bay field. In cases of pipeline investment we will assume a cost of equity capital of 15 percent and a long-term interest rate of 9.0 percent, with a 20 percent/80 percent equity to debt ratio. The weighted average cost of capital for the pipelines is:

(1) Method of Financing	(2) Proportion	(3) Cost after Taxes	(4) Weighted Cost (2x3)
Debt	.80	4.5%	3.6%
Equity	.20	15.0%	3.0%
		Weighted Average Cost of Capital	6.6%

A value of 7.0 percent will be used for trunk pipeline investments.

DEVELOPMENT OF THE FIELD

Much has been written concerning the high cost of operations on the North Slope. It is indeed true that the present cost of operating on the North Slope is very high. At the present time the cost of shipping supplies to Prudhoe Bay by air from Fairbanks is about $160 per ton, and this is probably the most efficient method of transport except for about three months during the summer when shipping can pass through the Arctic Ocean. However, an all-out effort was made in the summer of 1969 to build permanent harbor facilities at Prudhoe Bay in order to take advantage of much cheaper water transportation. Even though the Arctic Ocean is navigable for normal shipping only about three months per year, large quantities of drilling mud, fuel, chemicals, cement, oil-well casing, machinery, and vehicles could be brought in by water during the summer and stockpiled for later use. Until now, water transport to Point Barrow has been used only sparingly in drilling operations because of the problems involved in trying to make supply requirements coincide with the shipping season in the Beaufort Sea. The existence of a permanent, long-term project will now allow for long-range planning of supply needs. The savings in transportation costs through use of water transport will be especially important for the heavy investments needed in establishing permanent facilities at Prudhoe Bay and in developing the field.

Cost of Development Wells

The cost of individual wells in Prudhoe Bay field can be estimated with fair accuracy. As a starting point for estimation of well costs, the cost of 11,500-feet development wells in Swanson River field in southern Alaska can be used. Swanson River field wells are reported to have cost $550,000 each in the early 1960's. The time necessary to drill to 9,000 feet on the North Slope, the contract rates for drilling rigs, and the costs of transporting supplies are fairly well known. The costs for fuel for heating and rig power (which normally run about $2,000 per day during winters on the North Slope) will be small because oil and gas from the early wells will be used for fuel for subsequent wells.

The basic cost for a vertical development well in the field, exclusive of road and location costs, is estimated to be $600,000. Because well locations and roads are expensive on the North Slope, the field will probably be developed from "drilling islands." From each drilling island, five wells could be drilled on 640-acre spacing. One well would be drilled vertically and the other four would each be deviated one mile. For a field with a surface area of 100 ± square miles, about 70 miles of roads should be sufficient. The cost of gravel roads, four feet thick, has been estimated at between $125,000 and $250,000 per mile. The author has elected to use a cost of $200,000 per mile. Thus a total cost of $14,000,000, or $140,000 per well, would apply to a 100 ± square mile field. In addition to the regular field roads, the "drilling islands" are assumed to be gravel pads 600 feet long and 150 feet wide. This would provide slightly over two acres for five wells, and the cost is estimated at $250,000 or $50,000 per well. This brings the total well cost to an average of $790,000 each, but this would be the case for all vertical holes. The extra cost involved in deviating a well one mile is estimated at $75,000. As four-fifths of the wells would be directionally drilled, an average directional drilling cost of $60,000 is allocated to all wells. A total cost, therefore, of $850,000 per well is used for the wells drilled on 640-acre spacing.

When the operators drill infill wells at a later date on 320-acre spacing the average well cost should be reduced to $800,000, due to the need for less road building.

The one remaining large unknown in the development of the field is the average capacity of the producing wells, and therefore the total number of wells that will be drilled. Atlantic Richfield has released information that both wells completed thus far have had tests on which they flowed at daily rates of just under 2,500 barrels per day. Testimony at a hearing held by the State of Alaska on November 13, 1969, in Anchorage, brought out estimates that many wells in the field will have initial capacities of 10,000 barrels per day.

The total number of wells to be drilled in the field is a direct function of the average daily capacity of the wells. The operators have asked for temporary approval from the State of Alaska to develop the field on 640-acre spacing. Such a wide spacing implies large capacity wells in order to reach a productive capacity of 1.5 million barrels per day (the peak producing rate needed to deplete a field of 7.5 billion barrels in approximately 25 years). The operators will probably develop the field initially on 640-acre spacing and then drill infill wells on 320-acre (or smaller) spacing as additional productive capacity is needed. With reported pay thickness of over 400 feet, even a well on 160-acre spacing could easily have over 10 million barrels of reserves (with recovery factor of 200 barrels/acre foot, total reserves equal $160 \times 400 \times 200 = 12,800,000$ barrels). Because of the thick pay section, the gravity of the oil, the great size of the accumulation, and the fact that each of the first two wells has a capacity of at least 2,300 barrels per day, the author feels that the wells in the field will have high capacities. In the basic model of the field used in this paper, the average capacity of new wells is assumed to be 4,000 barrels per day.

The Field Model

For purposes of economic analysis, a model of Prudhoe Bay field, has been made which incorporates the following assumptions:

1. Total producible reserves are 7½ billion barrels of oil, none of which is offshore (it appears likely that the oil accumulation actually does extend offshore, but such reserves are not considered here).

2. Producing rates will be high by American standards—averaging 4,000 barrels per day per well initially, and no artificial lifting will be required in the early life of the field.

3. Most of the produced gas will be reinjected into the reservoir after being stripped of liquids in a natural gasoline plant.

4. Production will begin in mid-1972 and will reach a peak plateau in 1976. After 50 percent of total reserves have been produced an annual rate of decline of 12 percent is assumed. (Individual wells decline from the time of initial production, but continuous development drilling prevents decline in field production until 50 percent of reserves have been produced).

5. Taxes, royalties, depreciation schedules, and allowances are assumed to remain constant over the life of the field. Federal income taxes are assumed to be at a constant 50 percent rate for the life of the field. Percentage depletion is assumed to be at a rate of 20 percent of gross production but not exceeding 50 percent of net profits on any one lease. Production or severance taxes imposed by the

State of Alaska are ignored in the basic model, but will be discussed later.

6. A terminal value of zero is used for the field at the end of economic oil production even though a multi-trillion cubic feet gas field will probably remain.

7. The field will never be subjected to curtailment of production by either a state regulatory agency or any other party.

The objective of the field model is to determine the *minimum* price at which the crude oil could be sold (at the "wellhead") and still provide the producing companies their required rate of return (15 percent). The starting point for the model is taken as the middle of 1968, and all expenditures and revenues are discounted to a present value as of July 1, 1968. All cash flows in any calendar year are treated as though they occurred on July 1 of that year.

A word of explanation must be added here concerning the sources of cost estimates and producing practices which are used in the model of the field. In some cases estimated costs have been released in press reports by the field operators, but in most cases the cost estimates are merely those which would apply in the "southern 48" with a factor added for the additional expenses of operating on the North Slope. The additional expenses due to operating on the North Slope were estimated as follows: for oil field equipment, extra costs of 35 to 50 percent due to transportation and "winterizing"; for costs of installing equipment such as the crude oil gathering system and gasoline plant—100 percent extra; for costs due completely to labor—150 percent extra. The method of field development is based on general oil field experience as envisioned by the author and associates in the producing industry.

Table 6 lists the capital investments, operating costs, and petroleum production which have been assumed for the

TABLE 6

ALL VALUES ARE IN MILLIONS OF DOLLARS OR MILLIONS OF BARRELS

	68	69	70	71	72	73	74	75	76	77	78	79	80	81	82	83	84	85	86	87	88	89	90	91	92	93	94	95	96	97	98	Totals
Rig Mobilization Cost		1.8	1.8		.6																											4.2
Producing Wells	2.0	12.8	29.8	50.1	54.4	56.8	55.2	56.0	20.0	16.0	7.2	8.0	8.0																			376.3
Injection Wells	4.0		1.7	1.7	1.7	.8	.8																									10.7
Dry & Junked Wells		1.2	1.6	1.6	1.2	1.6	1.6	1.6	.8	.4	.4		.4																			12.4
Camp, Dock & Airstrip	3.2	4.2	12.4																													19.8
Vehicles	2.0	2.0	2.0	2.0	.3	.3	.3	.3		.1		.1		.1	.1	.1		.1	.1	.1	.1	.1										10.2
Power Plant			.5	1.5																												2.0
Automation Equip.				1.3																												1.3
Storage Tanks				5.0																												5.0
Gathering System				8.5	2.0	2.0	2.0	2.0																								16.5
Gasoline Plant			10.0	10.0		6.0																										26.0
Gas Injection System			5.0	15.0	20.0	20.0	20.0	20.0						20.0																		120.0
Artificial Lift Equipment													3.5	3.5	3.5	3.5																14.0
Storm Losses						5.0			5.0		5.0		5.0				5.0		5.0		5.0		5.0		5.0							45.0
Well Workovers									3.0	3.0	3.0	3.0	3.0	2.0	2.0	2.0	2.0	2.0	2.0	2.0	2.0	1.5	1.5	1.5	1.5	1.0	1.0	1.0	1.0			41.0
Field Operating Cost				2.5	5.5	9.0	9.0	10.4	10.8	11.0	11.0	11.0	11.0	11.0	11.0	11.0	11.0	11.0	11.0	10.8	10.7	10.5	10.3	10.1	10.0	10.0	10.0	10.0	10.0	10.0	10.0	279.6
Annual Oil Production				95	295	400	490	560	560	560	560	520	458	403	355	312	275	242	213	187	165	145	128	113	99	87	77	68	60	53		7480

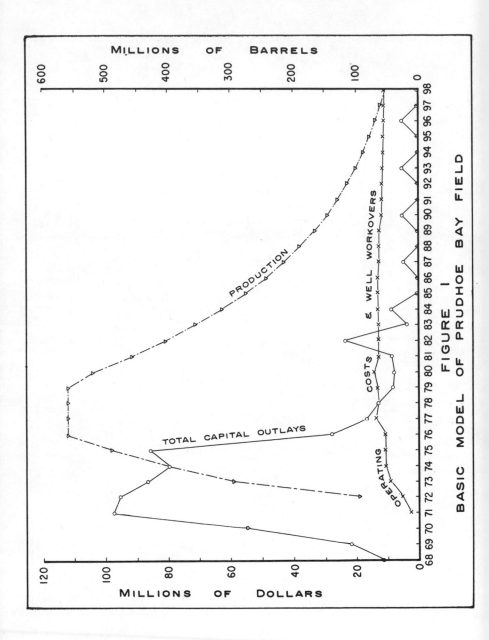

MILLIONS OF BARRELS

MILLIONS OF DOLLARS

PRODUCTION

& WELL WORKOVERS

COSTS

TOTAL CAPITAL OUTLAYS

OPERATING

FIGURE I

BASIC MODEL OF PRUDHOE BAY FIELD

basic field model, and Figure 1 shows the same data in graphic form. Total capital investment for developing the field is assumed to be $618 million ($207 million of which is considered as expenses for federal income tax purposes). An additional $368 million is assumed for storm losses, well workovers, and operating costs over the life of the field. Our problem now is to find the price at which the 7.5 billion barrels of crude oil could be sold at the wellhead such that all discounted cash outflows just balance all discounted cash incomes.

Costs Derived from the Model

The assumptions about the field stated previously and the data listed in Table 6 will be referred to as the Basic Model of the field. By processing the data in Table 6 and using the appropriate depreciation schedules, royalty rate, depletion allowance and income tax rates, and cost of the crude oil can be found. Table 7 is a detailed list of the computations involved in determining the present worth of the crude oil at Prudhoe Bay field. A price of $.28 per barrel is the minimum price for which the oil could be sold at the field and still provide a 15 percent return on all investments for the life of the field. Any additional severance tax that the State of Alaska might impose on the oil would have to be added to the $.28 in order for the operators to maintain a 15 percent rate of return.

At the risk of being overly repetitious, it is perhaps necessary to stress again that this figure ($.28 per barrel) is the cost of production only. The difference between the cost of production and the price at which the crude is actually sold at the field is divided between two categories—costs of exploration and profits. In the former category are the costs of exploration, including lease costs, which were expended in finding Prudhoe Bay field. In addition, exploration costs must include an allowance for unsuccessful ex-

Table 7

Present Worth of Prudhoe Bay Field at $28 per Barrel—Discounted at 15 Percent

	1968	1969	1970	1971	1972	1973	1974	1975
1. Rig Mobilization		1,800	1,800		600			
2. Producing Wells	2,000	12,750	29,750	50,150	54,400	56,800	55,200	56,000
3. Injection Wells	4,000		1,700	1,700	1,700	1,600	800	800
4. Dry and Junked Wells		1,200	1,600	1,600	1,200		1,600	1,600
5. Camp, Dock, and Airstrip	3,200	4,200	12,400					
6. Vehicles	2,000	2,000	2,000	2,000				
7. Power Plant			500	1,500	300	300	300	300
8. Automation Equipment				1,300				
9. Storage Tanks				5,000	2,000	2,000	2,000	2,000
10. Gathering System				8,500		6,000		
11. Gasoline Plant				10,000	10,000			
12. Gas Injection System			5,000	15,000	20,000	20,000	20,000	20,000
13. Artificial Lift Equipment								
14. Storm Losses					5,000			5,000
15. Well Workovers				2,500				
16. Field Operating Costs					5,500	9,000	10,400	10,800
17. Annual Crude Oil Production (000 bbls)					95,000	295,000	400,000	490,000
18. Total Capital and Operating Outlays (1 through 16)	11,200	21,950	54,750	99,250	100,700	95,750	90,325	96,450
19. Amount of 18 Expensible for F.I.T.	5,100	9,000	18,200	28,500	38,100	39,050	40,025	45,750
20. Crude Oil Revenue (17 × $.28)					26,600	82,600	112,000	137,200
21. Gasoline Production (000 bbls)					815	2,530	3,430	4,190
22. Gasoline Revenue (21 × $2.50)					2,038	6,335	8,575	10,475
23. Total Gross Revenue (20 + 22)					28,638	88,935	120,575	147,675
24. Net Revenue after Royalty (23 × .875)					25,118	77,818	105,503	129,216
25. Depreciation	491	1,224	3,337	7,061	12,076	16,796	21,196	25,330
26. Depletion (24 × .2) ≤ (.5 × {24 - 19 - 25})						10,986	21,101	25,843
27. Taxable Income (24 - 19 - 25 - 26)	(5,591)	(10,224)	(21,537)	(35,561)	(26,058)	10,986	23,181	32,293
28. Federal Income Tax (.5 × 27)	(2,796)	(5,112)	(10,769)	(17,781)	(13,029)	5,493	11,591	16,147
29. Net Cash Flow (24 - 18 - 28)	(8,404)	(16,838)	(43,981)	(81,469)	(62,553)	(23,425)	3,587	16,619
30. Discount factor @ 15%	1.000	.870	.756	.658	.572	.497	.432	.376
31. Present Worth (29 × 30)	(8,404)	(14,649)	(33,250)	(53,607)	(35,780)	(11,642)	1,550	6,249

All Values are in millions of dollars except where noted.

60

Table 7 (Continued)

#	Item	1976	1977	1978	1979	1980	1981	1982	1983
1.	Rig Mobilization								
2.	Producing Wells	20,000	16,000	7,200	8,000	8,000			
3.	Injection Wells	800	400	400		400			
4.	Dry and Junked Wells								
5.	Camp, Dock, and Airstrip								
6.	Vehicles		100		100		100		
7.	Power Plant								50
8.	Automation Equipment								
9.	Storage Tanks								
10.	Gathering System								
11.	Gasoline Plant								
12.	Gas Injection System								
13.	Artificial Lift Equipment						5,000	20,000	
14.	Storm Losses			5,000			3,500	3,500	3,500
15.	Well Workovers		3,000	3,000	3,000	3,000	2,000	2,000	2,000
16.	Field Operating Costs	11,000	11,000	11,000	11,000	11,000	11,000	11,000	11,000
17.	Annual Crude Oil Production (000 bbls)	560,000	560,000	560,000	560,000	520,000	458,000	403,000	355,000
18.	Total Capital and Operating Outlays (1 through 16)	31,800	30,500	25,600	22,100	22,400	21,600	36,500	16,550
19.	Amount of 18 Expensible for F.I.T.	21,800	22,400	23,000	18,000	18,400	18,000	13,000	13,000
20.	Crude Oil Revenue ($17 \times \$.28$)	156,800	156,800	156,800	156,800	145,600	128,240	112,840	99,400
21.	Gasoline Production (000 bbls)	4,800	4,800	4,800	4,800	4,450	3,930	3,450	3,040
22.	Gasoline Revenue ($21 \times \$2.50$)	12,000	12,000	12,000	12,000	11,125	9,825	8,625	7,600
23.	Total Gross Revenue ($20 + 22$)	168,800	168,800	168,800	168,800	156,725	138,065	121,465	107,000
24.	Net Revenue after Royalty ($23 \times .875$)	147,700	147,700	147,700	147,700	137,134	120,807	106,282	93,625
25.	Depreciation	25,544	25,673	25,567	22,882	20,182	17,796	18,253	18,760
26.	Depletion ($24 \times .2) \leq (.5 \times \{24 - 19 - 25\})$	29,540	29,540	29,540	29,540	27,427	24,161	21,256	18,725
27.	Taxable Income ($24 - 19 - 25 - 26$)	70,816	70,087	69,593	77,278	71,125	60,850	53,773	43,140
28.	Federal Income Tax ($.5 \times 27$)	35,408	35,044	34,797	38,639	35,563	30,425	26,887	21,570
29.	Net Cash Flow ($24 - 18 - 28$)	80,492	82,156	86,303	86,961	79,171	68,782	42,895	55,505
30.	Discount factor @ 15%	.327	.284	.247	.215	.187	.163	.141	.123
31.	Present Worth (29×30)	26,321	23,332	21,319	18,697	14,805	11,211	6,048	6,827

61

Table 7 (Continued)

	1984	1985	1986	1987	1988	1989	1990	1991
1. Rig Mobilization								
2. Producing Wells								
3. Injection Wells								
4. Dry and Junked Wells								
5. Camp, Dock, and Airstrip	3,500							
6. Vehicles		50		50		50		50
7. Power Plant								
8. Automation Equipment								
9. Storage Tanks								
10. Gathering System								
11. Gasoline Plant								
12. Gas Injection System								
13. Artificial Lift Equipment								
14. Storm Losses	5,000			5,000			5,000	
15. Well Workovers	2,000	2,000	2,000	2,000	2,000	2,000	1,500	1,500
16. Field Operating Costs	11,000	11,000	11,000	10,800	10,700	10,500	10,300	10,100
17. Annual Crude Oil Production (000 bbls)	312,000	275,000	242,000	213,000	187,000	165,000	145,000	128,000
18. Total Capital and Operating Outlays (1 through 16)	21,500	13,050	13,000	17,850	12,700	12,550	16,800	11,650
19. Amount of 18 Expensible for F.I.T.	18,000	13,000	13,000	17,800	12,700	12,500	16,800	11,650
20. Crude Oil Revenue (17 × $.28)	87,360	77,000	67,760	59,640	52,360	46,200	40,600	35,840
21. Gasoline Production (000 bbls)	2,670	2,360	2,070	1,820	1,600	1,420	1,240	1,100
22. Gasoline Revenue (21 × $2.50)	6,675	5,900	5,175	4,550	4,000	3,550	3,100	2,750
23. Total Gross Revenue (20 + 22)	94,035	82,900	72,935	64,190	56,360	49,750	43,700	38,590
24. Net Revenue after Royalty (23 × .875)	82,281	72,538	63,818	56,166	49,315	43,551	38,238	33,766
25. Depreciation	19,246	19,253	19,239	19,246	18,527	14,629	12,394	8,464
26. Depletion (24 × .2) ≤ (.5 × {24 - 19 - 25})	16,456	14,508	12,762	9,560	9,044	8,201	4,522	6,753
27. Taxable Income (24 - 19 - 25 - 26)	28,579	25,777	18,817	9,560	9,044	8,201	4,522	6,949
28. Federal Income Tax (.5 × 27)	14,290	12,889	9,409	4,780	4,522	4,101	2,261	3,475
29. Net Cash Flow (24 - 18 - 28)	46,491	46,599	41,409	33,536	32,093	26,880	19,177	18,641
30. Discount factor @ 15%	.107	.093	.081	.070	.061	.053	.046	.040
31. Present Worth (29 × 30)	4,975	4,334	3,354	2,348	1,958	1,425	882	746

All Values are in millions of dollars except where noted.

62

Table 7 (Continued)

	1992	1993	1994	1995	1996	1997	1998	Totals
1. Rig Mobilization	1,500							4,200
2. Producing Wells								376,250
3. Injection Wells								10,700
4. Dry and Junked Wells								12,400
5. Camp, Dock, and Airstrip								19,800
6. Vehicles				50				9,850
7. Power Plant		50						2,000
8. Automation Equipment								1,300
9. Storage Tanks								5,000
10. Gathering System								16,500
11. Gasoline Plant								26,000
12. Gas Injection System								120,000
13. Artificial Lift Equipment								14,000
14. Storm Losses		5,000			5,000			45,000
15. Well Workovers		1,500	1,000	1,000	1,000	1,000	1,000	41,000
16. Field Operating Costs	10,000	10,000	10,000	10,000	10,000	10,000	10,000	281,600
17. Annual Crude Oil Production (000 bbls)	115,000	99,000	87,000	77,000	68,000	60,000	53,000	7,480,000
18. Total Capital and Operating Outlays (1 through 16)	11,500	16,550	11,000	11,050	16,000	11,000	11,000	985,625
19. Amount of 18 Expensible for F.I.T.	11,500	16,500	11,000	11,000	16,000	11,000	11,000	574,725
20. Crude Oil Revenue (17 × $.28)	31,640	27,720	24,360	21,560	19,040	16,800	14,840	2,094,400
21. Gasoline Production (000 bbls)	970	850	740	660	580	515	455	64,085
22. Gasoline Revenue (21 × $2.50)	2,425	2,125	1,850	1,650	1,450	1,288	1,138	160,213
23. Total Gross Revenue (20 + 22)	34,065	29,845	26,210	23,210	20,490	18,088	15,978	2,254,613
24. Net Revenue after Royalty (23 × .875)	29,807	26,114	22,934	20,309	17,929	15,827	13,981	1,972,786
25. Depreciation	6,341	4,529	3,021	1,509	1,001	601	414	410,582
26. Depletion (24 × .2) ≤ (.5 × {24 - 19 - 25})	5,961	2,543	4,457	3,900	464	2,113	1,284	370,187
27. Taxable Income (24 - 19 - 25 - 26)	6,005	2,542	4,456	3,900	464	2,113	1,283	616,363
28. Federal Income Tax (.5 × 27)	3,003	1,271	2,228	1,950	232	1,057	642	308,187
29. Net Cash Flow (24 - 18 - 28)	15,304	8,293	9,706	7,309	1,697	3,770	2,339	678,982
30. Discount factor @ 15%	.035	.030	.026	.023	.020	.017	.015	
31. Present Worth (29 × 30)	536	249	252	168	34	64	35	387

All Values are in millions of dollars except where noted.

ploratory ventures in other parts of the world (probably an unknowable figure even for an individual company). In the category of profits, we must include both company profits and profits to the State of Alaska in the form of several taxes. But the two subjects of exploration costs and profits are not our concern here, so let's get back to costs.

In an analysis of this kind, numerous questions arise concerning the validity of the data used in the model. For example, what would be the effect on the cost of production if the producing wells cost $1 million each instead of $850,000? A few sensitivity analyses have been made on the Basic Model in an attempt to answer some of these questions. Because the figure of $.28 per barrel is near the low end of the range of published estimates of Prudhoe costs, we shall only consider factors here which would raise that figure. (There are reasonable assumptions, such as average capacity of wells, which could lower the cost derived from the Basic Model by a large percentage. In terms of absolute amount, however, this large percentage decrease is not significant—amounting to less than 10 cents per barrel.) The sensitivity analyses are as follows:

1. *The Basic Model except that the discount rate is raised to 20 percent from 15 percent.* Discounting all future cash flows at 20 percent has the effect of raising the cost from $.28 per barrel to $.35 per barrel.

2. *The Basic Model* (using 15 percent discount rate) *except that all production is delayed one year.* That is, the production in any given year in this case is the amount listed in the Basic Model for one year earlier. This delay of production raises the cost to $.32 per barrel.

3. *The Basic Model except that an additional lump sum investment of $100 million is added in 1972.* This is assumed to be some capital investment with a 20-year life, so that an additional $5 million depreciation figure is also

used for the years from 1972 through 1991. This additional $100 million investment raises the cost of the crude oil to $.34 per barrel.

4. *The Basic Model, but with $10 million of additional field operating costs each year from 1968 through 1998.* The increase in cost here is to $.33 per barrel.

5. *The Basic Model modified by all factors in (1) through (4).* That is, the Basic Model is modified by a discount rate of 20 percent, production delayed one year, additional investment of $100 million in 1972, and $10 million added operating costs each year. The cost of the crude derived from the model when all these factors are taken together is $.58 per barrel.

The foregoing sensitivity analyses merely show what the effect is on the cost of production from the Basic Model if certain factors are changed. It is emphasized here that the Basic Model represents the author's "best estimate" of how the field will be developed, and that sensitivity analyses could just as easily have been made by changing factors which would have reduced the cost of production rather than raising it. What these analyses give us is a "reasonable" range of estimates which has a lower limit of $.21 per barrel, an upper limit of $.40 per barrel, and a "best estimate" of $.28 per barrel. The reader is welcome to take exception to the term "reasonable" and, of course, many people have already done so. Estimates for the cost of production of over $1.00 per barrel have appeared in industry trade publications. Anyone can play this game of estimation, but the price of admission should include some action highlights and not just an announcement of the final score.

One more analysis that can be made from the Basic Model is the present worth of the field (July 1, 1968) if a particular price for the oil is assumed. A number of people in the oil industry have speculated about what the price will be, and their estimates average about $1.75 per barrel. We shall assume a constant price of $1.60 per barrel, and plugging this into the Basic Model gives a present worth (15% discount factor) for the field of $1.1 billion as of July, 1968.

The present worth of the field at $1.60 per barrel presents an interesting comparison with the value which stock market investors seemed to be placing on the field in the late summer of 1968. Earlier, the assertion was made that investors seemed to evaluate Atlantic Richfield's half of the field at about $750 million in the first few weeks after the announcement of the discovery. The Basic Model suggests that Atlantic Richfield's share of the field was worth $550 million at an assumed price of $1.60 per barrel (also assuming that Atlantic Richfield's share of the field was about 4 billion barrels).

The value of $1.1 billion for the field at $1.60 per barrel also makes an interesting comparison with the $1.16 billion rise in the combined market values of the stocks of Jersey Standard and Atlantic Richfield on the first day that each was traded after the "5- to 10-billion-barrel" announcement (see p. 391).

TRANSPORTING CRUDE OIL

The operators of Prudhoe Bay field have several alternatives available to them in deciding the method to be used in transporting the oil to market. These alternatives involve various combinations of pipelines and/or tankers, but the various methods can be grouped into three general operations: (1) pipeline from the North Slope to southern Alaska and then by tanker to markets or to other pipeline terminals; (2) pipeline from the North Slope across Canada directly to markets in the midwestern United States; (3) directly by tanker from a Beaufort Sea loading facility to world markets.

The chief advantage of building a pipeline across Alaska to an ice-free port on the southern coast lies in the probability that it can be built with a minimum amount of delay due to technological or political reasons. Although the problem of laying pipe across the area underlain by permafrost is still under study, the operators are proceeding with construction plans and indicate that the pipeline will be finished in 1972. The main disadvantages of a trans-Alaskan pipeline stem from the fact that a minimum capital outlay of $900 million is required merely to bring the oil to a point on the Alaskan coast which is still 1,400 miles from the nearest sizable market (State of Washington). If the next few years bring forth a more economical method of transporting the crude, the owners of the pipeline could find themselves in the position of having to reduce pipeline tariffs to a level which would not provide an adequate rate of return on the invested capital.

A pipeline across Canada to the midwestern United States would put the oil directly into a large market whose nearby sources of crude oil are declining. However, a pipeline across Canada which transported Alaskan oil would probably raise questions about the entire Imports Control Plan. A public debate over the granting of a right-of-way for such a pipeline might cause the Canadian government to proceed cautiously on the subject, and any delay in starting the pipeline would result in loss of revenue to the operators of Prudhoe Bay field as they waited with their shut-in wells for an outlet. If other large fields are discovered in the future, either on the Alaskan North Slope or in the Canadian far-north, a trans-Canadian pipeline may be built.

All-year shipment of crude oil by tanker through the Arctic Ocean has not yet been proven feasible, but the recent voyage of the S.S. *Manhattan* through the Northwest Passage puts it in the realm of a distinct possibility. Such a method of transport would offer potentially large economic advantages. These potential advantages result from the relatively short distances involved in using the Northwest Passage for shipment to the U.S. East Coast and a polar route for shipment to Europe.

Trans-Alaskan Pipeline Method

Atlantic Richfield, Humble, and British Petroleum have already announced that their pipeline subsidiaries will build a 48-inch diameter pipeline from Prudhoe Bay to Valdez on the southern Alaskan coast. The press release stated that the construction cost will be $900 million for the pipeline and terminal facilities and that it would have an initial capacity of 500,000 barrels per day. A capacity of 500,000 barrels per day is far below the capacity of a 48-inch pipeline and industry sources have speculated on what the total investment in the pipeline will be when the necessary equipment has been installed in order to bring it to peak capacity. R. O. Anderson of Atlantic Richfield has stated that the line will eventually have a peak capacity of two million barrels per day.

As a starting point for analysis, the $900 million figure announced by Atlantic Richfield, Humble, and British Petroleum can be used as a base. According to the operators of the field, the $900 million will provide the minimum number of pumping stations and the minimum amount of terminal facilities required for moving 500,000 barrels per day through the line. In various newspaper and trade-journal publications, estimates have been made for the total cost of the pipeline when it is brought up to the 2 million barrels per day capacity. Such estimates center around $1.5 billion. In private conversations with pipeline engineers, the author has not found any large disagreement with the $1.5 billion estimate.

Because this paper has estimated the peak capacity of Prudhoe Bay field at 1.6 million barrels per day, that same capacity will be assumed for the trans-Alaskan pipeline. The assumption here is that a further increase in capacity of the pipeline to 2 million barrels per day would be based on an economic decision, i.e., if it looks profitable to increase capacity, it will be done. What we now need is the estimate of capital investment needed to bring the line up to a capacity of 1.6 million barrels per day from the initial investment of $900 million. The estimates of the previously mentioned pipeline engineers range between $250 million and $400 million. To be on the safe side, we will use the $400 million figure. Thus we are ready to develop a Basic Pipeline Model.

Pipeline Model

The following assumptions have been made for the Basic Pipeline Model:

1. An original investment of $900 million for completion of the pipeline and terminal facilities.
2. Additional investment of $400 million in order to bring capacity up to 1.6 million barrels per day.
3. Annual ad valorem taxes of 1.25 percent of original investment.
4. Direct operating costs (exclusive of taxes) average $.06 per barrel in the whole range of capacities from 750,000 barrels per day to 1.6 million barrels per day.
5. The average weighted cost of capital (after tax) is 7 percent, based on the following information:

(1) Method of Financing	(2) Proportion	(3) Cost after Taxes	(4) Weighted Cost (2x3)
Debt	.80	5%	4%
Equity	.20	15%	3%
		Average Weighted Cost =	7%

6. Depreciation charges for income tax purposes are on a straight-line basis over 25 years.
7. Income taxes are assumed to be at the 50 percent rate over the life of the project.
8. No terminal value is given to the facilities after 30 years, and no revenues are considered after 30 years.
9. The basic assumption is made that enough additional oil will be found on the North Slope to keep the pipeline

operating at peak capacity after Prudhoe Bay production declines below 1.6 million barrels per day, in other words, a total throughput of 14.3 billion barrels.

Costs Derived from the Model

Table 8 lists the data used in the Basic Pipeline Model. Again, the cost of transport is defined as the lowest price which could be charged for transport and still allow a return of 7 percent on all investments over the life of the project. The figure that satisfies this requirement is $.41 per barrel, which was used to determine the figures in the column under "Revenue" in Table 8.

We can now examine the sensitivity of this cost of transport to two different factors:

1. An additional capital investment of $200 million is needed in 1971. This would increase the cost of transport from $.41 per barrel to $.46 per barrel.

2. The assumption in the Basic Pipeline Model that the line operates at 1.6 million barrels per day after 1976 is changed so that the pipeline throughput declines in the same manner as field production does in the Basic Model of Prudhoe Bay.

This would mean that no oil other than the seven and one-half billion barrels from Prudhoe Bay field were transported through the line. This assumption would raise the cost of transport to $.60 per barrel. In view of the new discoveries announced after the September lease sale, the cost figure derived from this assumption is considered unrealistically high. So we have a range of pipeline costs from $.41 per barrel to $.60 per barrel. The "best estimate" lies between the $.41 figure for the Basic Pipeline Model and the $.46 figure derived from adding the $200 million investment to the Basic Model. The author considers $.45 per barrel as the most reasonable figure.

Table 8

Trans-Alaskan Pipeline Costs at $.41 per Barrel
Discounted at 7 Percent

Year	Capital Investment $000	Expenses $000	Depreciation $000	Volume 000 bbls	Revenue $000	Taxable Income $000	Income Tax $000	Net Cash Flow $000	Discount Factor	Present Worth $000
1968		2,000				(2,000)	(1,000)	(1,000)	1.0000	(1,000)
1969	20,000		800			(800)	(400)	(19,600)	.9346	(18,300)
1970	100,000		4,800			(4,800)	(2,400)	(97,600)	.8734	(85,200)
1971	530,000	4,000	26,000			(30,000)	(15,000)	(519,000)	.8163	(423,700)
1972	250,000	23,000	36,000	95,815	39,300	(19,700)	(9,850)	(223,850)	.7629	(170,800)
1973	200,000	33,000	44,000	297,530	122,000	45,000	22,500	(133,500)	.7130	(95,200)
1974	200,000	41,000	52,000	403,430	165,400	72,400	36,200	(111,800)	.6663	(74,500)
1975		47,800	52,000	494,190	202,600	102,800	51,400	103,400	.6228	64,400
1976		53,000	52,000	564,800	231,600	126,600	63,300	115,300	.5820	67,100
1977		53,000	52,000	564,800	231,600	126,600	63,300	115,300	.5439	62,700
1978		53,000	52,000	564,800	231,600	126,600	63,300	115,300	.5084	58,600
1979		53,000	52,000	564,800	231,600	126,600	63,300	115,300	.4751	54,800
1980		53,000	52,000	564,800	231,600	126,600	63,300	115,300	.4440	51,200
1981		53,000	52,000	564,800	231,600	126,600	63,300	115,300	.4150	47,800
1982		53,000	52,000	564,800	231,600	126,600	63,300	115,300	.3878	44,700
1983		53,000	52,000	564,800	231,600	126,600	63,300	115,300	.3625	41,800
1984		53,000	52,000	564,800	231,600	126,600	63,300	115,300	.3387	39,100
1985		53,000	52,000	564,800	231,600	126,600	63,300	115,300	.3166	36,500
1986		53,000	52,000	564,800	231,600	126,600	63,300	115,300	.2959	34,100
1987		53,000	52,000	564,800	231,600	126,600	63,300	115,300	.2765	31,900
1988		53,000	52,000	564,800	231,600	126,600	63,300	115,300	.2584	29,800
1989		53,000	52,000	564,800	231,600	126,600	63,300	115,300	.2415	27,800
1990		53,000	52,000	564,800	231,600	126,600	63,300	115,300	.2257	26,000
1991		53,000	52,000	564,800	231,600	126,600	63,300	115,300	.2109	24,300
1992		53,000	52,000	564,800	231,600	126,600	63,300	115,300	.1972	22,700
1993		53,000	52,000	564,800	231,600	126,600	63,300	115,300	.1843	21,200
1994		53,000	51,200	564,800	231,600	127,400	63,700	114,900	.1722	19,800
1995		53,000	47,200	564,800	231,600	131,400	65,700	112,900	.1609	18,200
1996		53,000	26,000	564,800	231,600	152,600	76,300	102,300	.1504	15,400
1997		53,000	16,000	564,800	231,600	162,600	81,300	97,300	.1406	13,700
1998		53,000	8,000	564,800	231,600	170,600	85,300	93,300	.1314	12,300
Totals	1,300,000	1,369,800	1,300,000	14,281,365	5,856,100	3,186,300	1,593,150	1,593,150		(2,800)

TANKER SHIPMENT

In this paper, the cost of shipping oil by tanker means the cost of shipping it by tanker under long-term charter. Various trade publications print tanker rate information, but for shipments from Alaska very little information is available. Therefore, the author has used information derived from personal communications with members of the tanker industry, and also previous studies which have derived "rules of thumb." Also, because the location of the southern terminal of the trans-Alaskan pipeline is not yet known, distances listed are only approximate.

One of the most important factors affecting tanker rates is the limitation imposed on shipments between United States ports by the Jones Act. The Jones Act requires that all shipments made between one U.S. port and another U.S. port must be made in ships built and registered in the United States. Because of the higher costs of construction and operation of U.S. ships, the cost of shipment between U.S. ports is much greater than would be the case if foreign-flag shipping were used.

A study of *Petroleum Press Service* has provided a rough "rule of thumb" for foreign-flag tanker rates on hauls of about 6,000 miles.[6] It states that costs per barrel per thousand miles for a 50,000 dwt tanker are $.07 to $.08; for a 100,000 dwt tanker $.05 to $.06; for a 200,000 dwt tanker $.035 to $.04; and for a 300,000 dwt tanker $.025 to $.03. Members of the shipping industry have said privately that for U.S. registered ships the above costs should be doubled. These cost figures will be our "rules of thumb."

Costs to District V Points (California, Oregon, Washington)

Industry sources have predicted publicly that by 1972, new tankers in the 70,000-ton category are likely to reduce the Gulf of Alaska to Los Angeles cost to $.25 per barrel.

As a rough check on this $.25 per barrel estimate the "rules of thumb" can be applied. The distance from the Gulf of Alaska to Los Angeles is approximately 2,200 nautical miles. Using a cost of $.07 per barrel for a 50,000-ton tanker, the cost per barrel would be (2.2 × $.07), or $.154 per barrel for foreign-flag shipping and $.31 per barrel for U.S. shipping. The estimate of $.25 per barrel for a 70,000-ton tanker, therefore, appears to be in good agreement with the "rules of thumb." The range of estimates the author has received from private sources for the Gulf of Alaska to Los Angeles run was between $.25 per barrel and $.41 per barrel. The author will use a "best estimate" of $.30 per barrel for the run to Los Angeles; $.25 per barrel to the San Francisco Bay area; and $.20 per barrel to the Puget Sound area. When the trans-Alaskan pipeline costs are added to these tanker costs, total transportation costs of $.75 per barrel are derived for transport to Los Angeles. This total amount is $.15 per barrel more than is estimated by Walter Levy, as quoted by Main.[7]

Cost to Philadelphia Area

Main states that industry sources believe oil could be shipped from Valdez to Philadelphia via the Panama Canal for $1.00 per barrel. A 65,000-ton tanker is about the maximum-sized tanker which can pass through the Panama Canal, and the trip from Alaska to Philadelphia is about 7,100 nautical miles. If the "rules of thumb" are applied to this distance using a $.14 per barrel per thousand miles cost for a 50,000-ton U.S. tanker, a cost of $1.05 per barrel is derived—including canal tolls and delays. If a cost of $.12 per barrel per thousand miles is assumed for a 65,000-ton U.S. tanker, a cost of about $.90 per barrel is derived for the Alaska to Philadelphia run.

A different method of delivering the oil to Philadelphia would be cheaper, but it would probably have to enter the

U.S. under the import quota. The method would be to ship the oil from Alaska to Panama in foreign-flag supertankers, and then unload it on the Pacific side of Panama. The oil would then be shipped by pipeline (which would have to be built) across Panama and loaded on another foreign-flag tanker. Private sources estimate the two tanker runs would cost a total of about $.40 per barrel including the extra offloading and onloading on the trip. No study has been made by the author on the cost of a pipeline and facilities in Panama, or even whether the idea is legally or politically feasible. However, from a comparison with the cost anaysis of the 800-mile trans-Alaskan pipeline, it appears that the cost of transport in a trans-Panama pipeline would definitely not be over $.10 per barrel. Using these costs, Prudhoe Bay crude could be delivered in Philadelphia for a total cost of $1.23 per barrel as foreign crude (including production costs).

Cost to Japan

When shipment of Alaskan oil to Japan is considered, the very large economies of scale associated with foreign-flag supertankers become apparent. The shipping distance from the Gulf of Alaska to Yokohama is approximately 3,000 nautical miles. Using the "rule of thumb" from the *Petroleum Press Service* study, a cost of $.04 per barrel per thousand miles on a 200,000-ton tanker gives a tanker cost of $.12 per barrel to Japan. Private sources of the author gave estimates from $.10 per barrel to $.18 per barrel. The average of these estimates was $.16 per barrel. Using a cost of $.16 per barrel would give a total cost of $.89 per barrel ($.28 producing cost plus $.45 pipeline cost plus $.16 tanker cost) for the crude delivered in Yokohama by 200,000-ton tankers, and probably $.04 per barrel less by 300,000-ton tankers.

PIPELINE ACROSS CANADA

Trade journals had speculated, before the operators announced their intention of building the trans-Alaskan pipeline, that the Prudhoe Bay oil might be transported by pipeline across Canada and be marketed in the Chicago area. If more large fields are found on the North Slope, the Canadian route may still be used. The general plan discussed by the trade journals would involve laying a 1,600-mile line up the Mackenzie River valley to Edmonton, Alberta, where it would connect through the Interprovincial Pipeline System with the Chicago area. Of course, the Interprovincial System would have to be expanded to take care of the added flow.

The cost of transporting oil from the North Slope to Chicago has been estimated by some industry sources, but these estimates are very questionable because it is doubtful that any engineered surveys have been made of the possible route. For example, the *Oil and Gas Journal* speculated that a line to Chicago might cost $1.5 billion. *Oilweek* quoted Jack Gallagher, president of Dome Petroleum, as saying on November 15, 1968, that the 1,600 miles of line from Prudhoe Bay to Edmonton could be built for $600 million. Levy has estimated the cost of transporting the crude by pipeline to Chicago at $.80 to $1.00 per barrel.[8] The author has no reliable data to use with which he could make a reasonable estimate of the costs of a North Slope-Chicago Line, so no evidence will be given to support any cost figure. However, while warning the reader that the following figure is actually only guesswork, a cost of $.75 per barrel for transporting oil from the North Slope to Chicago seems reasonable.

DIRECT TANKER TRANSPORT FROM PRUDHOE BAY

Many magazine and newspaper articles have been written concerning the possibility of shipping Prudhoe Bay oil directly from Alaska's north coast through Arctic Ocean routes to world markets. The potential impact on the East Coast markets of the U.S. and even the European market is very large if Arctic Ocean ice problems can be licked.

The 1969 voyage of the S.S. Manhattan through the Northwest Passage proved the possibility, if not the economic feasibility, that ice-breaking supertankers may be able to move oil from Prudhoe Bay directly to the U.S. East Coast. Humble Oil and Refining officials were generally optimistic after the Manhattan's voyage and were even quoted as estimating the cost at $.90 to $1.00 per barrel for moving oil to the U.S. East Coast.

SUMMARY AND CONCLUSIONS

Production Costs

The estimated cost of producing Prudhoe Bay crude oil, derived from the model in this thesis, is about $.28 per barrel. For this figure to be a realistic estimate, three primary assumptions must hold true. The first is that the wells in the field must have an average productive capacity of close to 4,000 barrels per day each. The second assumption that must hold is that there will be no big delays past the 1972 target date in getting the field into production, and after it's in production the field will not be shut down or have its production cut back by proration.

The $.28 per barrel cost figure does not include any severance tax imposed by the State of Alaska. The cost of producing the crude must take this into account, and the severance tax (based on selling price—not cost) must be added to the cost figure of this paper.

Transportation Costs

The cost of transporting crude oil from Prudhoe Bay to the southern Alaskan coast is estimated to be between $.41

per barrel and $.60 per barrel. This wide range in estimates is due to a different assumption for the pipeline model. The cost of $.60 per barrel is derived by assuming that only seven and one-half billion barrels of crude from the Prudhoe Bay field will ever be shipped through the pipeline. The $.41 per barrel cost is derived by assuming that oil from other fields or extensions will be shipped through the line so that once the pipeline reaches a capacity of 1.6 million barrels per day, it will continue at that capacity throughout its lifetime (27 years).

Tanker costs from the southern Alaskan coast are dependent on the long-term charter rates of the future. This paper has relied on people in the shipping business for estimates of tanker rates. The "best estimate" figures used for shipment from a southern Alaskan port are $.30 per barrel to Los Angeles; $.25 per barrel to San Francisco; $.20 per barrel to Seattle; and $.12 per barrel to Yokohama.

Total Costs

The total cost of the oil (exclusive of severance taxes) delivered in various ports is given by Table 9. For each destination the "low," "high," and "expected" costs are given for production and transportation. Tanker rates are estimated long-term charter rates in U.S.-flag tankers except for the run to Yokohama and the "foreign oil" run to Philadelphia. The "expected" costs are expected only in the sense that they represent the author's best estimates of the costs.

Conclusions

The cost of Prudhoe Bay crude oil is low enough to compete under the present pricing pattern for markets anywhere in the United States. It could also compete with Persian Gulf oil in Japanese markets under the present

Table 9

Total Costs of Prudhoe Bay Oil
Delivered at Various Ports

Port	Production Cost/bbl.	Transportation Pipeline	Cost/bbl. Tanker	Total Cost/bbl. Delivered
Los Angeles				
Low	$ .21	$ .41	$ .25	$ .87
High	.40	.60	.41	1.41
Expected	.28	.45	.30	1.03
San Francisco				
Low	.21	.41	.21	.83
High	.40	.60	.36	1.36
Expected	.28	.45	.25	.98
Seattle				
Low	.21	.41	.17	.79
High	.40	.60	.31	1.31
Expected	.28	.45	.20	.93
Philadelphia				
Low	.21	.41	.90	1.52
High	.40	.60	1.05	2.05
Expected	.28	.45	.95	1.68
Philadelphia *				
Low	.21	.51	.40	1.12
High	.40	.70	.40	1.50
Expected	.28	.55	.40	1.23
Yokohama				
Low	.21	.41	.10	.72
High	.40	.60	.18	1.18
Expected	.28	.45	.12	.85

* As foreign oil, and with $.10 per barrel included in pipeline costs for shipment by pipeline across Panama.

price pattern of approximately $1.50 per barrel in Japan. This does not mean, however, that Prudhoe Bay crude will move into all of these markets. The actual marketing of Prudhoe Bay crude will depend on (1) how much more oil is found in Alaska and Canada, and (2) the future pattern of regulations imposed by state, federal, and foreign governments.

NOTES

1. L. F. Davis, "Economic Planning and Judgment in North American Exploration," *Journal of Petroleum Technology,* June 1968.
2. M. J. Gordon and E. Shapiro, "Capital Equipment Analysis: The Required

Rate of Profit," *The Management of Corporate Capital,* edited by Ezra Solomon (Glencoe, Ill.: The Free Press, 1959).

3. M. Miller and F. Modigliani, "Dividend Policy, Growth and the Valuation of Shares," *Journal of Business,* October 1961, pp. 411-433.

4. R. Crowell, "Earnings Expectations, Security Valuation, and the Cost of Equity Capital," M.I.T. Sloan School of Management, Ph.D. Thesis, 1967.

5. J. E. White, "Economics of Scale Applies in Long Distance Pipeline Transport," *Oil and Gas Journal,* January 27, 1969, pp. 149-156.

6. *Petroleum Press Service,* "Pipelines Versus Tankers," 35:2, February 1968, pp. 59-60.

7. Jeremy Main, "The Hot Oil Rush in Arctic Alaska," *Fortune,* 79:4, April 1969, p. 123.

8. *Ibid.*

Estimated Wellhead and Delivered Costs of North Slope Alaska Crude

Cabinet Task Force on Oil Import Control

Much of what can be pieced together about production and delivery from the Arctic is somewhat speculative at this stage. Nevertheless, reasonable estimates of relevant magnitudes—to the extent that they are available—should help indicate the probable competitiveness of domestic oil in world markets when production from that source enters the market.

Because of the potential importance of Alaskan crude oil and the dearth of publicly disclosed cost projections, the Task Force staff has attempted on the basis of available evidence to construct its own estimates of the cost (both at the wellhead and at various ports) of North Slope crude. All assumptions and estimates will be explicitly stated so that those with better information may so advise the Task Force. The calculated wellhead cost is exclusive of all lease payments.[1]

On February 16, 1968, Atlantic Richfield (ARCO) announced that its Prudhoe Bay State No. 1 exploratory well (spudded in on April 22, 1967), located on the Alaskan North Slope two miles from the shores of the Arctic Ocean, had encountered both oil and gas. The zones were in a Triassic sand body 470 feet thick, the base of which was encountered at 8,078 feet.[2] Four months later, on June 25, 1968, ARCO announced that its second well (Sag River State No. 1), drilled seven miles southeast of Prudhoe Bay State No. 1, had encountered crude in the same Triassic formation as the initial well. ARCO also announced that on a production test Prudhoe Bay State No. 1 had produced as much as 2,415 barrels of 30.5 degree API gravity crude per day.[3] Finally, on July 18, 1968, ARCO chairman Robert O. Anderson quoted the following statement from a DeGolyer and MacNaughton study: "In our opinion this important discovery could develop into a field with recoverable reserves of some five to ten billion barrels of oil, which would rate as one of the largest petroleum accumulations known to the world today."[4] At the same time, Mr. Anderson also announced that Sag River State No. 1 had encountered 300 feet of oil sand in the same formation as Prudhoe Bay State No. 1; moreover, the Sag River well had produced 2,300 barrels per day.

Even without additional North Slope oil, which most oilmen feel certain will also be discovered, this evidence shows that the Prudhoe Bay discovery is very large. A further indication of its great size was recently revealed when ARCO's Mr. Anderson announced plans by a consortium to spend at least $900 million to build a 48″ pipeline between the North Slope and Valdez on the Alaskan Gulf. After initial completion in 1972 this pipeline would carry 500,000 barrels per day. Mr. Anderson also indicated that its throughput would quickly be increased up to its designed capacity of 2 million barrels per day.[5] In addition, Humble is spending large sums to test the feasibility of bringing Arctic oil to the U.S. East Coast via the Northwest

Passage, a Mackenzie Valley pipeline to the Canadian and American Midwest has been proposed, and studies have also been launched of the feasibility of building a pipeline from Seattle to Chicago and perhaps the East Coast.[6] In these circumstances, it is assumed that the Prudhoe Bay field contains 10 billion barrels of recoverable reserves.[7]

Although the North Slope has enormous potential, both its present developers (ARCO and Humble) and others have stressed that there will also be enormous costs in producing crude from a tundra plain located 390 miles north of Fairbanks. The Task Force is interested in assessing the likely cost of producing crude in this "hostile" environment and the cost of shipping it to market. This study attempts two tasks: first, an estimate of the price at which crude from a hypothetical North Slope field containing recoverable reserves of 10 billion barrels could be sold at the wellhead and still yield its developers a specified minimum rate of return on all invested capital; second, some estimates of the delivered cost of North Slope crude from this hypothetical field. To preview the conclusions of these calculations: it appears that North Slope crude could be sold at the wellhead for about $0.36 per barrel.[8] Moreover, at mid-1969 delivered prices, North Slope crude could be competitive with foreign crude at any point in the continental United States, Japan, or Northern Europe.

WELLHEAD COSTS

In order to estimate North Slope wellhead costs, three facts must be ascertained:

1. What will be the annual output of crude?
2. What total expenditures (and on what time-stream) will be necessary in order to produce this crude? This would include both investment and operating costs.
3. What is the general return on the capital thus invested?

The Cost of Capital

These calculations postulate an annual after-tax return of 15 percent on the capital invested in North Slope production and development. This 15 percent figure—and higher discount rates for domestic investments are seldom used—compares with the U.S. petroleum industry's average 1968 rate of return on invested capital of 12.9 percent.[9]

Projected Annual North Slope Crude Output

The assumptions of this study are:

1. Output begins in mid-1972 at an annual rate of 500,000 barrels per day.
2. Output builds up gradually so that it averages: 700,000 barrels per day in 1973; 1 million barrels per day in 1974; 1.5 million barrels per day in 1975; 2 million barrels per day in 1976.
3. Output remains at a peak of 2 million barrels per day through 1981 (when cumulative output is 5.52 billion barrels).[10] Thereafter it declines at an annual rate of 10 percent.

The implications of these assumptions are summarized in Table 10. In addition, the conservative assumptions are made that (1) the invested capital and mineral rights of this field are worthless once the estimated recoverable reserves are exhausted in late 1992; and (2) that no revenue arises from the sale of gas. Thus, the field's total revenue may be understated with the result that costs would, to that extent, be overstated.

Total Wellhead Costs of North Slope Crude

To estimate the total wellhead costs (the minimum price that just repays capital costs) of North Slope crude, one

Table 10

Annual Crude Output from a North Slope Field

Year	Annual Output (million barrels)	Daily Average Output (million barrels)	Cumulative Annual Output (million barrels)
1972	91	0.25	91
1973	256	0.7	347
19/4	365	1.0	712
1975	548	1.5	1,260
1976	730	2.0	1,990
1977	730	2.0	2,720
1978	730	2.0	3,450
1979	730	2.0	4,180
1980	730	2.0	4,910
1981	730	2.0	5,640
1982	657	1.8	6,297
1983	591	1.62	6,888
1984	532	1.46	7,420
1985	479	1.31	7,899
1986	431	1.18	8,330
1987	388	1.06	8,718
1988	349	0.95	9,067
1989	314	0.85	9,381
1990	283	0.76	9,664
1991	255	0.68	9,919
1992	81	0.22	10,000

must first determine the average initial rate of decline. The study assumes an initial flow of 5,000 barrels per day at each time period for the average well and an annual decline rate of 10 percent.[11] Although this estimate of initial well flow is consistent with that in other giant fields, it is far lower than a published estimate that the average Prudhoe Bay well would produce 15,000 to 20,000 barrels per day.[12] This assumption implies the results summarized in Table 11.

It is now in order to examine the cost of developing a 10-billion-barrel North Slope field.

1. Gross 1968 exploration costs are assumed to have been $40 million. This sum may seem excessive in comparison with the $10 million estimated total cost of the two

Table 11

Number of Wells Needed to Develop a 10-Billion-
Barrel North Slope Field,
Assuming an Initial Well Flow of 5,000 Barrels Per Day

Year	Number of New Producing Wells	Number of New Dry Wells	Cumulative Number of Producing Wells
1969	10	2	10
1970	20	4	30
1971	30	6	60
1972	40	8	100
1973	50	10	150
1974	74	15	224
1975	120	24	344
1976	130	26	474
1977	40	8	511
1978	40	8	551
1979	40	8	591
1980	40	8	631
1981	40	8	671
1982	0	0	671
1983	0	0	671
1984	0	0	671
1985	0	0	671
1986	0	0	671
1987	0	0	671
1988	0	0	671
1989	0	0	671
1990	0	0	671
1991	0	0	671
1992	0	0	671

successful Prudhoe Bay wells. But the Prudhoe Bay developers had several dry wells before striking crude. This study assumes that the total cost of such unsuccessful exploration did not exceed $30 million. To compute the federal income tax factor, the $40 million gross exploration cost is assumed to include (a) $7.5 million in capital items depreciated on a straightline basis over 20 years and (b) $32.5 million to be currently expensed.

2. The development cost attributable to the average North Slope producing well is assumed to be $1.5 million. This figure would include the costs of rig mobilization, producing wells, injection wells, housing facilities, airport,

transportation vehicles, 5-foot-thick gravel roads, 5-foot-thick gravel drilling beds, any costs of well deviation, power plant, gathering system, and lift equipment.[13]

3. Twenty percent of all new wells are assumed to be dry. The average cost of each is assumed to be $1.0 million.

4. Annual nonallocable operating costs for a 10-billion-barrel field are assumed to be $15 million. These expenditures are assumed to begin in 1972.

5. The average annual allocable cost of operating a well is assumed to be $10,000.

6. It is assumed that:

> a. Of the total average producing-well development costs of $1.5 million, 60 percent ($900,000) is expensed for federal income tax purposes in the year paid. The remainder is capitalized.
>
> b. The annual average cost of operating any well ($10,000) is also currently expensed for federal tax purposes.
>
> c. All costs for dry wells are currently expensed for federal tax purposes.
>
> d. Capital costs are depreciated for federal income tax purposes on a straightline basis for 20 years. At a faster rate of depreciation, the discounted tax savings would be larger and thus the calculated wellhead cost would be lower.

7. Closing the field is assumed to cost the companies $50 million in 1992.

8. Severance taxes are assumed to amount to 10 percent of the gross wellhead total revenue of North Slope crude. This is higher than current Alaskan severance taxes and appears to be higher than severance taxes in any other state.

9. After payment of royalties, 87.5 percent of total wellhead revenue (after severance taxes) is assumed to be retained by the producers.

10. The depletion allowance is assumed to be the smaller of either 27.5 percent of the producers' retained revenues

(item #9 above) or 50 percent of the producers' retained revenues minus all currently expensable expenditures and depreciation.

11. It is assmued that the State of Alaska does not prevent production at maximum efficient rates through market demand prorationing.

12. The Jones Act is taken into account.

Given the foregoing assumptions, a wellhead price has been calculated that will cover current and capital costs plus a 15 percent after-tax return on all expenditures. Table 12 summarizes this calculation. It shows that on the stated assumptions (at least some of which appear conservative) the wellhead cost of North Slope crude could be $0.36 per barrel.[14]

THE DELIVERED COST OF NORTH SLOPE CRUDE

Initial plans for the Prudhoe Bay field call for its output to be shipped by pipeline from the North Slope to Valdez, Alaska. The pipeline owners—the Trans-Alaskan Pipeline System (a joint venture of the Atlantic Pipeline Company, the Humble Pipeline Company, and the BP Pipeline Corporation—estimated that a pipeline capable of carrying 500,000 barrels per day by 1973 will require a $900 million investment.[15] Estimates appearing in the trade press suggest that an additional investment of $600 million will be required to raise the line's capacity to 2 million barrels per day. Assuming very high operating costs (because of severe weather and rugged terrain), the per barrel pipeline costs would probably not exceed $0.45.[16] If so, the maximum cost of North Slope crude delivered to Valdez would be $0.81 per barrel.

To compute the delivered cost of North Slope crude to points of consumption, we must add all transport costs from the North Slope. Assumptions of transport costs—often somewhat higher than those appearing in the litera-

Table 12

Wellhead Cost of North Slope Crude
(All cost figures are in millions of dollars)

Year	(1) Gross Annual Development Expenditures for Producing Wells	(2) Gross Annual Expenditures for Dry Wells	(3) Gross Annual Operating Expenditures	(4) Total Depreciation	(5) Total Items Expensed	(6) Gross Annual Output (Million barrels)	(7) Annual Output after Severance Taxes (Million barrels)	(8) Annual Output Accruing to Producers after Royalties (Million barrels)	(9) Gross Annual Outlays
1968	$40.0	$0	—	$0.4	$32.5	—	—	—	$40.0
1969	15.0	2.0	—	0.7	11.0	—	—	—	17.0
1970	30.0	4.0	—	1.3	22.0	—	—	—	34.0
1971	45.0	6.0	—	2.2	33.0	—	—	—	51.0
1972	60.0	8.0	$16.0	3.4	60.0	91	81.9	72	84.0
1973	75.0	10.0	16.5	4.9	71.5	256	230	201	101.5
1974	111.0	15.0	17.3	7.1	98.9	365	328	287	143.3
1975	180.0	24.0	18.4	10.7	150.4	548	493	431	222.4
1976	195.0	26.0	19.7	14.6	162.7	730	657	575	240.7
1977	60.0	8.0	20.1	15.8	64.1	730	657	575	88.1
1978	60.0	8.0	20.5	17.0	64.5	730	657	575	88.5
1979	60.0	8.0	20.9	18.2	64.9	730	657	575	88.9
1980	60.0	8.0	21.3	19.4	65.3	730	657	575	89.3
1981	60.0	8.0	21.7	20.6	65.7	730	657	575	89.7
1982	0	0	21.7	20.6	21.7	657	591	517	21.7
1983	0	0	21.7	20.6	21.7	591	532	466	21.7
1984	0	0	21.7	20.6	21.7	532	479	419	21.7
1985	0	0	21.7	20.6	21.7	479	431	377	21.7
1986	0	0	21.7	20.6	21.7	431	388	340	21.7
1987	0	0	21.7	20.6	21.7	388	349	305	21.7
1988	0	0	21.7	20.2	21.7	349	314	275	21.7
1989	0	0	21.7	19.9	21.7	314	283	248	21.7
1990	0	0	21.7	19.3	21.7	283	255	223	21.7
1991	0	0	21.7	18.4	21.7	255	229	200	21.7
1992	0	0	71.7	74.2	71.7	81	73	64	71.7

Column 1 is equal to $40 million in 1968. Thereafter it is equal to $1.5 million times the number of new producing wells.

Column 2 is equal to $1.0 million times the number of new dry wells.

Column 3 is equal to $15.0 million plus $10,000 times the number of producing wells. By assumption this cost begins in 1972.

Column 4 is calculated on the assumption that beginning with 1969, 40 percent of all entries in column 1 are capital costs. We assume straightline depreciation, 20-year life.

Column 5 is equal to the sum of 60 percent of column 1, column 2, and column 3.

Column 6 is the gross annual output of the field.

Column 7 is equal to column 6 times 0.9.

Column 8 is equal to 0.875 times column 7.

Column 9 is equal to the sum of columns 1, 2, and 3.

Year	(10) Depreciation + Expensed Items	(11) Total Revenue When P = $0.36	(12) Total Depletion Allowance	(13) Total Tax Deductibles	(14) Total Taxable Income	(15) Total Income Tax	(16) Total Net Cash Outlay	(17) Net Cash Flow	(18) Discounted Net Cash Flow (r = 0.15)
1968	$32.5	—		$32.5	($32.5)	($16.3)	$24.1	($24.1)	($24.1)
1969	11.7	—		11.7	(11.7)	(5.8)	11.2	(11.2)	(9.7)
1970	23.3	—		23.0	(23.3)	(11.7)	22.3	(22.3)	(16.9)
1971	35.2	$25.9		35.2	(35.2)	(17.6)	33.4	(33.4)	(22.0)
1972	63.4	72.4		63.4	(37.5)	(18.8)	65.2	(39.3)	(22.5)
1973	76.4	103.3		76.4	(4.0)	(2.0)	99.5	(27.1)	(13.5)
1974	106.0	155.2		106.0	(2.7)	(1.8)	141.5	(38.2)	(16.5)
1975	161.1	207.0		161.1	(5.9)	(2.9)	219.5	(63.8)	(24.1)
1976	177.3	207.0		192.1	14.9	7.4	248.1	(41.1)	(13.3)
1977	79.9	207.0	$14.8	136.8	70.2	35.1	123.2	83.8	23.8
1978	81.5	207.0	56.9	138.4	68.6	34.3	122.8	84.2	20.8
1979	83.1	207.0	56.9	40.0	67.0	33.5	122.4	84.6	18.2
1980	84.7	207.0	56.9	141.6	65.4	32.7	122.0	85.0	15.9
1981	86.3	207.0	56.9	143.2	63.8	31.9	121.6	85.4	13.9
1982	42.3	186.1	51.2	93.5	92.6	46.3	68.0	118.1	16.6
1983	42.3	167.8	46.1	88.4	79.4	39.7	61.4	106.4	13.1
1984	42.3	150.8	41.5	83.8	67.0	33.5	55.2	95.6	10.2
1985	42.3	135.7	37.3	79.6	56.1	28.0	49.7	86.0	8.0
1986	42.3	122.4	33.7	76.0	46.4	23.2	44.9	77.5	6.3
1987	42.3	109.8	30.2	72.5	37.3	18.6	40.3	69.5	4.9
1988	41.9	99.0	27.2	69.1	29.9	15.0	36.7	62.3	3.8
1989	41.6	89.3	23.8	65.4	23.9	12.0	33.7	55.6	2.9
1990	41.0	80.3	19.7	60.7	19.6	9.8	31.5	48.8	2.2
1991	40.1	72.0	16.0	59.8	12.2	6.1	27.8	44.2	1.8
1992	145.9	23.0		145.9	(122.9)	(61.5)	10.2	12.8	0.4
								Total	$0.2

Column 10 is equal to the sum of columns 4 and 5.
Column 11 is equal to $0.36 times column 8.
Column 12 is the smaller of 27.5 percent times column 11 or 50 percent of column 11 minus column 10.
Column 13 is the sum of columns 10 and 12.
Column 14 is equal to column 11 minus column 13.

Column 15 is equal to 0.50 times column 14.
Column 16 is equal to the sum of columns 15 and 9. In any given year this sum is the actual out-of-pocket expenses of the field's developers.
Column 17 is equal to column 11 minus column 16.
Column 18 is equal to column 17 discounted at 15 percent.

ture—are presented in Table 13. [17] (Shipping costs between Valdez and U.S. ports will exceed Valdez-Japan costs by the incremental cost of using U.S.-flag ships, which are made mandatory by the Jones Act for carriage between U.S. ports.)

Table 13

Costs of Crude Oil Transport

From	To	Cost (Per Barrel)
Valdez	Los Angeles	$0.30
Valdez	U.S. East Coast (via Panama Canal)	1.00
Valdez	Yokohama, Japan	0.15
Valdez	Chicago (via Seattle)	0.55
North Slope	Valdez	0.45
North Slope	Chicago	1.00
North Slope	U.S. East Coast (via Northwest Passage)	0.60
North Slope	Northern Europe (via Northwest Passage)	0.40

Table 14

The Delivered Cost of North Slope Crude

Location	Delivered Cost (Per Barrel)
Los Angeles	$1.11
Chicago	1.36
U.S. East Coast (via Northwest Passage)	0.96
U.S. East Coast (via Panama Canal)	1.81
Yokohama, Japan	0.96
Northern Europe	0.76

CONCLUSION

Table 14 summarizes the results of this discussion. It shows estimates of the delivered cost of North Slope crude. It appears that at current world prices, North Slope crude could be sold competitively at any point in the continental United States even if all U.S. oil import quotas were removed. Moreover, at these prices, and assuming Humble's estimate of traversing the Northwest Passage to be correct,

North Slope crude could be sold competitively in both Northern Europe and Japan.

In conclusion, it should be emphasized that the above estimates represent a best guess of what would be the per barrel costs (assuming a 15 percent after-tax rate of return on all invested capital and ignoring all lease costs) of crude from a field like that of Prudhoe Bay. The estimated wellhead cost is obviously tentative although it is premised largely on the statements of the Prudhoe Bay developers. It is worth noting, however, that doubling or perhaps even tripling this estimate (which would allow for considerable variation in a number of assumptions made here) would still permit Alaskan crude to compete, at current world prices, with Middle Eastern oil at any place in the continental United States [18] or in Northern Europe.

These estimates remain subject to revision in the light of better data or more persuasive analysis. However, pending such detailed illumination, a reasonable order of magnitude is suggested by the estimates.

NOTES

1. Lease costs, bonuses, etc., are highly variable. The bonuses that oil companies are willing to offer in the future will depend on their expectations of net income flow from the properties developed, over and above costs and the minimum necessary return on investment. These lease costs are indeed costs from the viewpoint of the producing company that must pay them in order to bid leases away from possible competitors. They are left out of account here because we wish to calculate the cost of resources used in developing and producing Arctic oil—the minimum outlay required, including necessary return on capital. Any lease costs are in addition to these resource costs. Hence, our calculations are not a forecast of future prices.

2. *Wall Street Journal,* "Atlantic Richfield Obtains Oil Sample From Test Well," February 19, 1968.

3. *Wall Street Journal,* "Atlantic–Humble Oil Arctic Joint Venture Discovers Oil and Gas," June 26, 1968.

4. *Wall Street Journal,* "Alaska Oil, Gas Find Is Potentially Vast, Consulting Firm Says," July 19, 1968.

5. *Oil & Gas Journal,* "Group Discloses Plans for 48-Inch Pipeline From Prudhoe Bay," 67:7, February 17, 1969, pp. 42-43.

6. *Oil & Gas Journal,* "Assault on the Northwest Passage Nears," June 9,

1969, pp. 37-38; *Wall Street Journal,* "Three Oil Companies to Study Feasibility of Building First Coast-to-Coast Pipeline," July 24, 1969.

7. DeGolyer and MacNaughton, in their Task Force submission (for the Office of Science and Technology) state: ". . . an estimate of recoverable reserves of 50 billion barrels of oil and 280 trillion cubic feet of gas is not unreasonable for Alaska."

8. This is not to say that North Slope crude would actually sell at this well-head price. The point is that it could sell at this price and still yield a 15 percent after-tax return on all invested capital (given the assumptions stated below).

9. From data compiled by First National City Bank, presented in testimony by Edward Symonds before the Senate Subcommittee on Antitrust and Monopoly, March 22, 1969. This figure is computed by dividing all after-tax American oil industry profits by the book value of all oil industry equity capital. We do not know the rate actually used by these firms to discount their investments for internal planning purposes.

10. It has been suggested that the postulated speed of the field's development is too fast. Estimates by informed observers of likely output from the Prudhoe Bay field range from a low of 1.0 million to a high to 2.5 million barrels per day in 1975. For 1980, the range of North Slope output estimates has been between 2.5 and 5.0 million barrels per day. By 1975 there will be large sunk costs in North Slope transport facilities, and this (plus possible discoveries by many other oil companies including some that do not presently possess large crude supplies in the "lower 48") suggests that there will be strong economic pressures for rapid development of the area.

11. It has been suggested that wells with the postulated initial flow would possibly decline at less than 10 percent annually. If so, this study would, to that extent, overstate wellhead costs.

12. Jeremy Main. "The Hot Oil Rush in Arctic Alaska," *Fortune,* April 1969.

13. The estimate that average development expenditures are $1.5 million per well seems reasonable. ARCO's 1968 *Annual Report* (p. 12) says that "exploratory drilling on the North Slope might cost between six and seven times that done on land in California." Since the average onshore California oil well in the 7,500 10,000-foot depth bracket costs about $200,000, one might infer that the average Prudhoe Bay producing well would cost $1.4 million (7 × $200,000 = $1.4 million). Jack F. Bennett, General Manager of Humble's Supply Department, was cited by *The Journal of Commerce,* July 23, 1969, as saying "Operating costs are about $18 thousand per day for an Arctic drilling rig as compared to $10 thousand per day for an offshore rig in the Gulf of Mexico and $3 thousand per day for a conventional rig in West Texas." These ratios are consistent with ARCO's cost estimates.

14. Mr. M. A. Wright, president of Humble, in recent testimony before the Senate Subcommittee on Antitrust and Monopoly (May 22, 1969), stated: "We expect that Humble's investment in the North Slope will approach $400 million before we produce and sell our first barrel of Alaskan oil in 1972." For a similar field Table 11 estimates total development costs by 1972 of $211 million. The apparent discrepancy between this estimate and Mr. Wright's may be explained by the fact that Mr. Wright includes Humble's share of expenditures for the Trans-Alaskan pipeline and its

attempt to open the Northwest Passage. These elements probably total more than $300 million.

15. *Oil & Gas Journal,* "Trans-Alaska System Selects Route," June 9, 1969, pp. 39-40.

16. The Department of Interior's submission to the Task Force on Question 42 states that: "The line will have an ultimate capacity of two million barrels per day. At such throughput, costs might be as low as about 30 cents per barrel. However, at one million barrels per day the costs might be about 60 cents per barrel." An ARCO representative testified before the Alaskan Legislature that Trans-Alaska pipeline costs could be $0.75 to $1.00 per barrel for the 1972-1980 period. Because the basis of ARCO's estimate is not explained, this paper uses the median of the Interior Department's range.

17. ARCO's submission to the Task Force (p. 15) estimates marine transport costs from Valdez to Los Angeles to be $0.25 to $0.30 per barrel. Humble's *Arctic Tanker Test Presentation* (delivered in Houston, Texas, in January 1969) estimates total transport costs between the North Slope and the U. S. East Coast (via the Northwest Passage) to be $0.60 per barrel. This result is not very sensitive to large changes in capital costs; for example, an increase of $100 million in terminal investment raises costs only $0.036 per barrel. Nevertheless, it must be recognized that Humble's figure is tentative. The estimated transport cost to Northern Europe was derived by adjusting the Humble estimate of transport costs to the U. S. East Coast by the lower cost of foreign-flag shipping. Jeremy Main in "The Hot Oil Rush in Arctic Alaska" (*Fortune*, April 1969) reported petroleum trade press estimates of the cost of transport from the North Slope to Chicago ranging between $0.80 and $1.00 per barrel. He also cited an estimate that oil could be sent from Valdez to the East Coast (via the Panama Canal) at $1.00 per barrel. The petroleum trade press has suggested that the cost of shipping crude from the North Slope, via Valdez and Seattle, to Chicago would be about the same as the cost of direct shipment from the North Slope via a proposed Mackenzie Valley pipeline. This implies that the cost of shipping crude from Valdez to Chicago is about $0.55. Finally, given the short distance between Japan and Valdez and the very low cost of large foreign-flag tankers, transport between Valdez and Yokohama, Japan, is estimated to cost less than $0.15 per barrel.

18. With the possible exception of the East Coast via the Panama Canal (See Table 12).

Exploration Models and Petroleum Production Economics[*]

Paul G. Bradley [†]

COSTS OF PETROLEUM PRODUCTION

The importance that Alaska assumes as a supplier of crude petroleum will be measured by the amounts of crude that can be profitably produced at prevailing market prices. Unfortunately for our forecasting ability, the construction of a conventional long-run supply schedule for an extractive industry is a hard task. It requires calculation of a unit cost figure which summarizes the expenditures required at the margin in order to deliver a barrel of crude. Put slightly differently, the required figure imputes to production the factor costs necessary to maintain successively more expensive increments of output. In the long-run context these

* Some portions of this study appeared in different form in a paper prepared for the 20th Alaska Science Conference, University of Alaska, August 24-27, 1969. Helpful suggestions have been received from a number of people, most of whom are cited in connection with their own work. Special acknowledgment is due my colleague at the University of British Columbia, Dr. Russell Uhler, with whom earlier research on exploratory drilling in Alberta was jointly carried out.

† Paul G. Bradley is Associate Professor of Economics at the University of British Columbia in Vancouver, Canada.

outlays include what is required to maintain a desired level of underground stocks, as well as current production. Therefore, while some expenditures serve to increase current output or capacity at a given site, others primarily affect the location and manner of obtaining future output. It is these complicated relations between output and the various requisite expenditures that make the calculation of crude production costs difficult. Our theory of long-run costs in an extractive industry is incomplete, but it is adequate to support valuable empirical work.

With regard to the cost of producing crude petroleum, tradition favors separation of the production process into three activities: finding (or exploration), development, and lifting (or extraction). Rather than comprising a sequence of independent steps, these are in reality interrelated and subject to some degree of substitution. Thus an operator may elect early in the productive life of a reservoir to install pressure maintenance, for example, a water injection system. He thereby increases development cost (by investing more to secure added producing capacity and additions to proved reserves), but at the same time he reduces lifting cost (by postponing, possibly forever, putting his wells on pump). Similarly, when he drills an outpost well, he simultaneously explores (learns about the productive structure) and develops (again, secures added producing capacity and additions to proved reserves).

When estimating total production cost the analyst may make simplifying assumptions that are acceptable within prescribed limits but not otherwise. For example, finding costs, falling into the difficult realm of investment in knowledge, are frequently ignored as far as numerical cost estimates are concerned [1] or dealt with indirectly.[2] For an area where an operator has an extremely large quantity of probable reserves, as in parts of the Middle East, exploration investment will be small relative to investment made for the primary purpose of developing producing capacity. Hence, to a good approximation finding costs can be ignored. In some cases, and again the Middle East can serve as an example, the fields are extremely prolific producers, so the lifting cost component becomes relatively small, justifying quite gross estimating methods.[3]

For a new area such as the Alaska North Slope early estimates of total long-run production cost are important in establishing whether the area is likely to become a major supplier of crude petroleum. For just such an area, however, the finding cost component is appreciable and may remain so. A great deal of the drilling taking place seeks primarily to obtain knowledge. Companies are willing to invest large sums to gain information about the probable volume of oil-in-place and the likely fraction that can be recovered. This study will be concerned primarily with the exploration phase of petroleum production.

JOINT RETURNS TO DRILLING

To demonstrate the need for economic models of petroleum exploration, it is necessary to examine more closely the nature of petroleum production costs. Ignoring the possible substitutability of investment and lifting (or operating) costs, consider in isolation the investment required to produce crude oil. This principally takes the form of drilling expenditures, together with companion expenditures required for supporting surface facilities. In accordance with the notion of stages of production mentioned earlier, wells are commonly classified as either exploration or development, the former with several subcategories.

Development investment creates the asset proved reserves, which consists of producing capacity and an inventory of producible crude.[4] Alternatively, this asset may be portrayed as a time profile of future crude production. It is apparent, in this perspective, that the returns to development investment cannot be characterized in a single dimension. It makes a difference whether the investment that has created, say, 10 million barrels of proved reserves, permits production at an initial rate of 500 barrels per day, declining very slowly, or at 2,500 barrels per day, declining rapidly. Conversely, a reservoir producing 2,500 barrels per day is worth more if total producible reserves are 10 million barrels than if they number 2 million.[5]

Figures on development investment, as the papers in this volume demonstrate, can with certain assumptions be used to impute a unit cost to crude petroleum produced from a given reservoir, and hence to estimate an average cost which characterizes a region. In either case, of course, this cost differs from total production cost by being net of lifting cost and allowance for exploration expenditures. The former deficiency can be remedied by adding a margin for lifting cost, because in practice substitution possibilities between development investment and operating expense are limited. With exploration the problem is more difficult. Almost all drilling investment yields simultaneously proved reserves and producing capacity and information about probable reserves. Development and exploration are, like the bindweed and the honeysuckle, inextricably entwined. Rather than being separate activities, they are joint in variable proportions.

Table 15

The Relative Magnitudes of Types of Output from Various Classes of Drilling

Type of Well (Lahee classification)	Increment to Capacity, $\frac{dq_0}{dI}$	Increment to Proved Reserves, $\frac{dV}{dI}$	Increment to Knowledge $\frac{dT}{dI}$
Stratigraphic	0	0	+ +
Exploration			
new field wildcats	+	+ +	+ +
new pool wildcats deeper pool tests shallower pool tests	+	+ +	+
outposts	+	+ +	+
Development	+ +	0 or +	0

Table 15, which requires some explanation, illustrates the intermingling of exploration and development investment in practice. Wells are classified according to the standard AAPG or Lahee system shown in the first column.[6] For a particular increment of drilling investment, dI, let dU equal the corresponding value of all benefits obtained. Then:

$$dU = \frac{\partial U}{\partial q_0} dq_0 + \frac{\partial U}{\partial V} dV + \frac{\partial U}{\partial T} dT \qquad (1)$$

where $q_0 =$ increment of new producing capacity,
$V =$ volume of new proved reserves,
$T =$ a measure of knowledge gained.

Producing capacity and proved reserves have been identified with development investment; acquisition of knowledge, with exploration investment. Table 15 characterizes the relative magnitudes of each type of benefit for an increment of investment in each of the various recognized classes of wells. For example, with outpost wells the emphasis is on adding to proved reserves, but at the same time gains are sought in both producing capacity and information about the structure. The relative magnitudes assigned in the table are a matter of judgment, rather than explicit analysis.

How are we to proceed in the task of estimating the cost of producing petroleum in a particular region? It will probably be necessary to continue to utilize the conventional though imperfect three-way classification, looking separately at development and exploration costs. If so, an important question to be asked of exploration models should now be evident. Is it possible to define exploration in such a way as to be able to relate expenditures to benefits? If so, a measure of exploration cost is possible. Such a measure, it must again be emphasized, rests on the assumed separability of the two activities, exploration and development, and we have already observed that in practice such a separation can be only approximate. The estimation of exploration cost, and hence evaluation of the potential of a particular region, can be expected to present problems for new producing areas, such as the North Slope, which are quite different from those of established producing regions.

EXPLORATION AS SEARCH FOR
PROBABLE RESERVES

Exploration has been described so far as "learning about the productive structure" or as "obtaining information about probable reserves." As a first step toward formulating a more precise working definition, consider the terms "probable reserves" and "possible reserves" as employed by petroleum companies. J. J. Arps [7] defines "probable primary reserves" as those "within the known geological limits of a productive reservoir, which are inferred from limited evidence of commercially producible oil or gas, but where the evidence is insufficient to qualify under the 'proved' definition." "Possibly primary reserves" are those "whose existence may be inferred from geological considerations but where available data will not support a higher classification." Similarly, C. K. Leith [8] defines "probable" reserves with reference to mineral ores as "extensions near at hand, where the conditions are such that ore will probably be found but where the extent and limiting conditions cannot be so precisely defined as for proved ore." "Possible ore" is that "where the relations of the land to adjacent ore bodies and to geologic structures warrant some presumption that ore will be found but where the lack of exploration and development data precludes anything like certainty of its actual location or extent."

In practice, when a reservoir of crude is discovered, the amount of proved reserves which is credited is far less than the amount which will ultimately be forthcoming. The drilling of development wells brings increases in proved reserves, designated as either "extensions" or "revisions."

The Alberta Oil and Gas Conservation Board [9] has published statistics which illustrate the growth in estimates of proved reserves year by year from the data of a discovery. This growth is shown in Table 16, which lists the average

Table 16

Appreciation of Proved Reserves

Years from End of Discovery Year	Average Ratio, Reserves at End of Indicated Period to Reserves at End of Discovery Year
0	1.00
2	3.23
4	4.23
6	5.24
8	6.59
10	7.06
12	8.19
14	8.52
16	9.04
18	9.04

Derived from Table V-3, Alberta Oil and Gas Conservation Board, *Reserves of Crude Oil, Gas, Natural Gas Liquids and Sulphur, Province of Alberta,* Report 69-18, December 31, 1968, pp. 142-43.

"appreciation factor" for a sample of 128 individual pools, representing 87 percent of the initial proved reserves in the province. For example, on the average, proved reserves 10 years after discovery had increased more than sevenfold from the volume credited at the end of the discovery year. The Committee on Statistics of Drilling of the American Association of Petroleum Geologists [10] provides annual estimates of the size ("ultimate recoverable reserves") of new fields discovered in the United States. The committee notes that these initial estimates are "not a substitute for the careful calculation of 'proved' reserves made by a reservoir geologist or an engineer after the field is developed." The estimates are predictions of what proved reserves will be, and have generally been low by about 20 percent. Prospective additions to proved reserves in the form of extensions and revisions would seem to conform to the Arps and Leith definitions of probable reserves. Estimating the stock of probable reserves is closely related to the problem of estimating the returns to exploration, and hence represents a possible application of statistical methods soon to be examined.

If development drilling functions to transform probable reserves into proved reserves, exploratory drilling may be similarly thought of as the creation of probable reserves, in particular the transformation of "possible reserves" into probable reserves. It is this process to which statistical models of exploration are primarily addressed. Two troublesome problems arise. The first relates to the jointness through time in the returns to exploration. Attention has been drawn by Adelman [11] to the fact that the gains to exploration are not captured solely by the few wells that hit oil; knowledge derived from dry holes yields benefits which are reaped when deciding where to drill in future periods. Such intertemporal effects will not be accounted for in a measure which relates discoveries to exploration investment in a particular period. Second, given the notion that exploratory drilling generates probable reserves, the necessity for going back one step further to account for the analogous expenditures that create "possible reserves" might be argued. The defense here must be an empirical one. Such expenditures (seismic surveys, e.g.) are relatively small, and as yet there appears to be no way to escape the subjective nature of estimates of "possible reserves."

We can now summarize exploration as it will be described in the several statistical models. This is done in Figure 2. The quantity of probable reserves is not known with certainty, so it is treated as a random variable, $\tilde{R}$, derived from the random variable, $\tilde{S}_i$, the volume of oil-in-place in a particular reservoir. The total of probable reserves depends upon the number of discovered reservoirs, N_{cum}, and their respective recovery factors, F_i, allowance

Figure 2

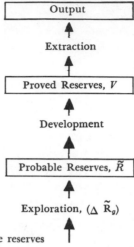

Notes: $R \equiv$ stock of probable reserves

$$\begin{array}{l} N_{cum} \\ = \Sigma\, F_i \tilde{S}_i \\ i = 1 \end{array} \left\{ \begin{array}{ll} N_{cum} & N_{cum} \\ \Sigma\, V_i + \Sigma\, P_i \\ i = 1 & i = 1 \end{array} \right\}$$

$(\Delta\, \tilde{R}g) \equiv$ gross additons to probable reserves through new discoveries

$$= \sum_{j=1}^{N} F_j \tilde{S}_j$$

where F_i (or F_j) = recovery factor
$\tilde{S}_i$ (or $\tilde{S}_j$) = oil-in-place in ith (or jth) reservoir, a random variable
V_i = proved reserves in ith reservoir
P_i = cumulative production to date from ith reservoir
N_{cum} = no. of reservoirs discovered to date
N = no. of new discoveries

being made for the volume of crude now classed as proved or already produced. The recovery factors depend on both physical and economic circumstances; in the present discussion we will assume an average recovery factor to be given, although it would be more appropriate to treat the recovery factor as a random variable.

Exploratory drilling yields additions to probable reserves

whose magnitude is not known in advance; this flow is
designated $(\triangle \tilde{R}_g)$ in Figure 2. The magnitude of a particular increment depends on the number of reservoirs found
by the corresponding program of exploratory drilling and
the size of the reservoirs. Most exploration models relate

Figure 3

Returns to Investment in Exploration

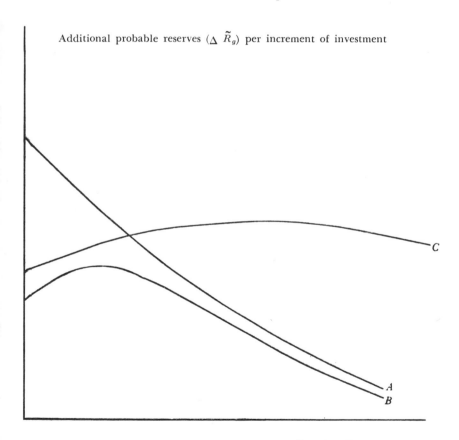

Additional probable reserves $(\Delta \; \tilde{R}_g)$ per increment of investment

Investment
(or number of wildcats)

to such incremental expansion of the stock of probable reserves.[12] The principal variables to be specified in these models, therefore, are $\tilde{N}$, the number of discoveries corresponding to a specified exploration investment, and $\tilde{S}$, the size of individual discoveries made. Before turning to a more detailed description of two types of such models it will be useful to consider several hypotheses regarding the nature of returns to investment in exploration.

For a particular region, the expected addition to probable reserves resulting from a specified amount of exploration activity will depend on such factors as the natural endowment of the region and current finding technology. It is also evident, however, that the size of the increment will depend on the amount of previous activity in the region and the knowledge available about the region. On the assumption that the best indicators provided by geophysical reconnaissance are explored first, incremental discoveries per dollar of investment would grow smaller over time because of stock depletion. On the other hand, as exploration proceeds, geological knowledge accumulates. At least for a time this effect may dominate, causing incremental discoveries to increase.

These possibilities are displayed in Figure 3, where three curves depict hypotheses about the yield to exploration investment over time in a given region. Curve *A* is the case where the best indicators are explored first; after the first round of wildcats, it's all downhill. Curve *B* is the case where the accumulation of knowledge about a region as drilling progresses more than offsets the using up of what were originally the best prospects. Hence an initial period of increasing incremental returns to drilling investment is observed, followed later by diminishing returns. Curve *C* is essentially similar, differing only in assuming that the region has a much larger number of reservoirs. All three hypotheses allow for eventual diminishing returns.

A MODEL OF THE OCCURRENCE AND SIZE OF
PETROLEUM RESERVOIRS

A principal, but not exclusive, objective of models of the search for petroleum is to bring available knowledge to bear to describe returns to exploration. With reference to Figure 3, we are concerned with the average height of the curves over selected intervals. If the returns to exploration are high, the exploration costs that must be imputed to crude produced in the region will be low; the opposite holds. Because the returns to exploration are uncertain, models of the process are stochastic, employing random variables of the sort defined in Figure 2.

No one has yet succeeded in confirming "the" model of petroleum or mineral exploration. We will consider two formulations of the problem. Each is indebted to the early work of Allais,[13] which grew out of an inquiry into the prospect of finding minerals in the Sahara. The first type of model is essentially that developed by Allais, as refined by later authors. The second type originated in the work of Arps and Roberts.[14]

One feature of Allais' work has been widely adopted subsequently. He hypothesized that the size distribution of mineral deposits was lognormal, that is, followed the probability function illustrated in Figure 4. The key feature of the lognormal distribution is its skewness; there is a bunching of small deposits, with a long tail to the right which represents the relative scarcity of very large deposits. Later researchers have tested this hypothesis with respect to crude petroleum reservoirs. The lognormal hypothesis was applied by Arps and Roberts to the Denver-Julesburg basin.[15] G. M. Kaufman in his study of statistical decision techniques in hydrocarbon exploration, dealt with methods for testing the hypothesis and provided examples using Canadian and U.S. statistics. He also discussed the rationale for the use of the distribution, that is, the characteristics

Figure 4

Lognormal Distribution of Pool Size

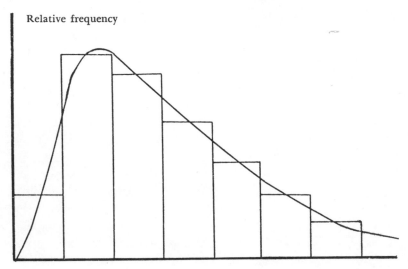

Relative frequency

Size, barrels of crude

of hydrocarbon formation which would yield such a distribution of deposits.[16] Recently a detailed study of petroleum reservoirs in Western Canada by R. G. McCrossan has provided support for the lognormal hypothesis, while drawing attention to the problem of classifying what may be, by virtue of geologic considerations, separate sets of data.[17]

The lognormal hypothesis is used in each type of model we will examine to describe the increment of probable reserves that results from a particular exploration investment, given the number of new reservoirs discovered. It is in their mechanisms for specifying the number of new discoveries that the two types of exploration model differ. Incidentally, the problem of estimating the size of newly discovered reservoirs is closely related to the problem described in the preceding section of estimating the total stock of probable reserves, that is, the proved reserves that will ultimately be forthcoming from fields now known but not yet developed. Application of statistical methods might well improve the procedures used by the AAPG Committee on Statistics of Drilling or the Oil and Gas Conservation Board for forecasting ultimate recoverable reserves from known fields.

Allais dealt with the problem of predicting the number of finds that would result from a particular exploration program by suggesting another hypothesis, that the indicators of deposits and, by implication, actual deposits, were distributed spatially according to the Poisson distribution. That is, if one considered sections of the region being studied, the number of deposits in a particular section

Figure 5

Poisson Distribution of Pool Occurrence

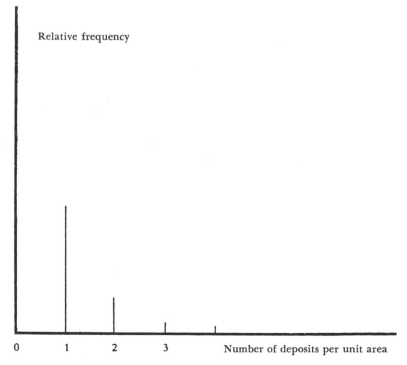

Relative frequency

0   1   2   3   Number of deposits per unit area

could be described by the probability functions shown in Figure 5. The combination of these distributions—one describing reserves conditional on number of finds and the other describing number of finds—thus specifies the behavior of the random variable, barrels of reserves per unit area of the basin.[18] Allais extrapolated data from other regions of the world in order to forecast the density of mineralization of the Sahara, i.e., to evaluate the Poisson parameter. Similarly, he extrapolated outside data in order to estimate the parameters of the lognormal distribution of deposit sizes, and then explored the properties of this distribution. He was thus able to estimate the expected returns to different-sized exploration programs and the probability of obtaining returns at least as great as various specified levels.

This approach has been applied in revised form to petroleum exploration by Uhler and Bradley.[19] A brief description of that work will demonstrate how this type of model works. Following Allais, to estimate total volume of petroleum to be found per unit of area, it is necessary to describe the volume of hydrocarbons per reservoir and the number of reservoirs per unit of area. The size of individual reservoirs, $\tilde{S}_i$, is by hypothesis a random variable with a lognormal distribution. The total reserves found per unit area, $\tilde{R}$, is a convolution of the $\tilde{S}_i$'s, that is, a random variable which is the sum of all the $\tilde{S}_i$'s. The number of $\tilde{S}_i$'s in the sum is itself a random variable, $\tilde{N}$, which by hypothesis has a negative binominal distribution. Thus: [20]

$$\tilde{R} = \sum_{i=l}^{\tilde{N}} F_i \tilde{S}_i. \qquad (2)$$

The reservoir recovery factors, F_i, are introduced to convert oil in place to recoverable reserves. As pointed out earlier, the recovery factor is properly a variable, but its specification is outside the scope of this analysis.

It does not appear possible to specify exactly the functional form of the distribution of reserves per unit area, $\tilde{R}$. However, the component distributions of equation (2) can be handled separately. Estimating their parameters permits calculation of the moments of the distribution of $\tilde{R}$, in particular, the mean and variance.

In testing this model with exploration statistics from Alberta, the objective is to confirm that its functional form —the selected combination of spatial occurrence and size distributions—fits actual observation. Available statistics, of course, refer to the reservoirs that have been discovered after a certain amount of exploration has occurred, rather than to all reservoirs actually present in nature. It is hypothesized that the model is applicable to regions which have been explored to various degrees. The values of its parameters change as exploration proceeds in a region, and will therefore correspond to the total reserves of the area only after an extremely large number of wildcats have

Table 17

Fits of the Poisson and Negative Binomial Distributions
to the Spatial Distribution of Oil Deposits for 5 x 5 Grid Areas

Deposits	Actual Frequency	Negative Binomial Frequency	Poisson Frequency
0	8586	8584.26	8508.53
1	176	176.84	303.01
2	35	39.09	5.40
3	13	11.25	0.06
4	6	3.62	0.00
5	1	1.23	0.00
6	0	0.44	0.00
7	0	0.16	0.00
8	0	0.06	0.00
9	0	0.02	0.00
10 or more	0	0.01	0.00

Negative Binomial $X^2 = 1.086$
Poisson $X^2 = 6365.91$

SOURCE: From R. S. Uhler and P. G. Bradley, "A Stochastic Model for Determining the Economic Prospects of Petroleum Exploration over Large Regions," paper presented to the Canadian Economics Association, Toronto, June 1960.

Table 18

Lognormality Tests of the Size of Oil
Reservoirs by Geologic Classification

Statistics	Calculated Value	Normal Value	Percentage Points of the Distribution of the Statistics	
			Upper (Lower) 5 percent	Upper (Lower) 1 percent
Limestone Reef (Biostrome)—Devonian			($m = 49$)	
A	.7818	.7979	(.7518)	(.7291)
B	.4078	.0000	.5340	.7870
C	3.0153	3.0000	3.9900	4.8800
Limestone Reef (Bioherm)—Devonian			($m = 94$)	
A	.8410	.7979	.8353 (X)	.8484
B	.1910	.0000	.4090	.5960
C	2.0951	3.0000	(2.3500) (X)	(2.1800) (X)
Limestone Reefs—Devonian			($m = 143$)	
A	.8292	.7979	.8282 (X)	.8390
B	.3321	.0000	.3210 (X)	.4640
C	2.3644	3.0000	(2.4500) (X)	(2.2900)
Sand—Cretaceous			($m = 290$)	
A	.7878	.7979	(.7781)	(.7693)
B	.9669	.0000	.2300 (X)	.3290 (X)
C	4.4714	3.0000	3.4700 (X)	3.7900 (X)
All Pools			($m = 540$)	
A	.8061	.7979	.8123	.8179
B	.7519	.0000	.1710 (X)	.2430 (X)
C	3.2720	3.0000	3.3500	3.5700

Key to Table 18: $A = M.D./(m_2)^{1/2}$
$B = m_3/(m_2)^{3/2}$
$C = m_4/(m_2)^2$
M.D. = mean deviation and
$$m_k = \frac{1}{n} \sum_{i=1}^{n} (x_i - x)^k$$

SOURCE: From P. G. Bradley and R. S. Uhler, "Economic Models of Petroleum Exploration," paper presented to the 20th Alaska Science Conference, Fairbanks, August 1969.

been drilled. Put another way, the parameter values used to calculate the reserves of a region are conditional upon the number of wildcats drilled (or the intensity of exploration).

Some of the results of testing the hypotheses of this model are displayed in Tables 17 and 18. For Table 17 the negative binomial parameters and the Poisson parameters were estimated from Province of Alberta data. The procedure involved arbitrarily demarcating the area of the sedimentary basin of Alberta into uniform subdivisions. The parameters estimated from this population were used to generate figures such as those shown in Table 16, which describe the relative frequency of reservoirs of a given size.[21] It is evident that use of the negative binomial function yields results which conform closely with the observed frequency of occurrence of reservoirs in Alberta, while use of the Poisson function does not.

The lognormal hypothesis was tested by conventional goodness-of-fit procedures, with results displayed in Table 18. With data for the entire population ("all pools" in Table 18) the lognormal hypothesis could be accepted at the one and five percent level for two of the test statistics used, but had to be rejected for the third. To remedy this shortcoming, an effort was made to improve the geologic controls used in specifying the model. If the lognormal hypothesis is only properly applied to reservoirs formed at similar times by similar processes, then correct specification requires separate examination of different structures.[22]

Further tests were then made after data had been classified according to the scheme shown in Figure 6. The results of these tests of the lognormal hypothesis also appear in Table 18. There is indication that goodness of fit of the lognormal distribution function does improve as data are classified according to finer geologic controls. Thus the best fit was observed for the class, "limestone reef (biostrome)—Devonian."

Figure 6

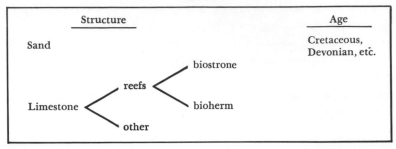

If the Allais-type model does win some confirmation when tested with available data, how is it applicable to the problem of estimating the returns to exploration? The Allais analysis involved the assumption that parameter values estimated from data for well-explored areas could be used to describe new areas. In the notation of Figure 2, Allais was concerned with determination of $\tilde{R}$, the probable reserves in an area. This type of model has several inherent limitations with respect to estimating the returns to exploration.

In the first place, exploration activity is depicted in Figure 2 as generating incremental additions to the stock of probable reserves, denoted $\triangle \tilde{R}_g$. These additions have the character of a flow, with magnitude dependent on the amount of exploratory drilling. The parameters of the Allais type of model, as just pointed out, are conditional on the amount of exploration that has taken place, and they summarize the cumulative results. Therefore, application of the model to generate estimates of incremental returns involves examining the changes in its parameters over time as exploration takes place. The model does not have a built-in theory of how the parameters change. It can be applied to predict returns over time in a particular area only by positing that the history of the "well-explored" reference area is repeated. The model's usefulness in predicting the results of exploration as they unfold over time is consequently rather limited. Of greater interest is its use to forecast the results of initial exploratory drilling in a new basin where the only knowledge at hand is derived from experience elsewhere.

For this type of between-regions extrapolation to be convincing, two conditions must be met. First, there must be evidence of geologic similarity, so that to a first approximation one can assume the density of hydrocarbon accumulation to be similar in both regions. Second, since the volume of probable reserves depends on the intensity of exploration, the extrapolation of a particular set of parameter values to a new basin implies a forecast of the reserves that will have been found in that basin when it is explored as intensively as the reference area; that is, all indicators of comparable quality are investigated in each area.

One reasonable application of a model of this type would be to generate predictions about returns to exploration in the Arctic by making use of the results of statistical analysis of Alberta data. To the extent that the process by which petroleum reservoirs were formed was the same in the two areas, extrapolation of Alberta parameter values will yield information about the Arctic. In light of the first condition for extrapolation mentioned above, note that one might initially rely on estimates for the North Slope area based on the sedimentary regions of Alberta. As geologic information becomes available, it would be possible to identify basins where the targets could be defined according to a more precise classification. If Devonian reefs were productive in a particular basin, for example, initial estimates of its potential could be based on experience with similar areas of that sort in Alberta.

The other condition relevant to the extrapolation of parameter values from Alberta to the Arctic related to specifying the intensity of exploration. If available geologic knowledge supports the initial assumption that the number of indicators is comparable in the two areas, then the intensity of exploration could be indexed by the number of wildcats drilled per unit area. Projections for an Arctic region based on extrapolating Alberta parameters would be valid only when a comparable number of wildcats had been drilled.

While the value of predicting the petroleum potential of a region by applying parameters estimated in other areas is limited, the model we have been discussing also provides a framework for the use of data from the new region as it becomes available. This has implications for applying statistical sampling techniques to the analysis and collection of data in the new region. Once a number of wildcats has been drilled, the results can be used to revise the parameter values that were originally assumed. A formal procedure for accomplishing this is the use of Bayesian analysis in estimating the parameters of the distribution function describing occurrence and reservoir size in the new area.[23]

A MODEL OF RETURNS TO EXPLORATION
IN A REGION

The second type of exploration model we wish to consider, the one associated with Arps and Roberts, is fundamentally different from the one just examined. Whereas the Allais-type model dealt with the spatial density of hydrocarbon occurrence, this approach concerns itself explicitly with returns through time to exploration in a particular region. This model is conveniently described using a formulation of Kaufman[24] and later Crabbé.[25]

The number of new pools of a given size discovered by an increment of new wildcats is:[26]

$$\frac{d}{dw}[N(w)f(a;w)]da = \alpha a[N(\infty)f(a;\infty) - N(w)f(a;w)]da \qquad (3)$$

In equation (3) $N(w)f[a;w)da$ is the number of fields of a given size (areal extent)[27] discovered by the first w wildcats; this expression is the product of the number of successful wildcats and the probability element representing the probability that a successful wildcat will discover a field of the given size. This model postulates that for an increment of wildcat drilling the number of discoveries that are of the given size depends on the terms on the right-hand side of equation (4), which are:

$\alpha =$ a constant reflecting available knowledge and technology,

$a =$ the areal extent (size) of the pools,

$N(\infty)f(a; \infty)da =$ the number of pools of the given size that would be discovered by an infinite number of wildcats, i.e., the number available to be found initially.

$N(w)f(a;w)da =$ the number of pools of the given size that have been discovered by the first w wildcats.

Thus discoveries of pools of a given size are postulated to be proportional to a real extent and to the number of undiscovered pools of that size.

Risking oversimplification, the model works like this. Equation (4) is integrated over a range, $w_2 - w_1$, of wildcats drilled. For a given size class of pool, the number of discoveries is observed. From this information it is possible to compute an estimate of the total number of pools present in that class, $N(\infty)f(a; \infty)da$. Taking account of all pool-size classes (by integrating over a) yields an estimate of the total number of pools in the region and their size distribution. It is also possible, using the assumption that pool sizes are lognormally distributed, to compute the probability that the next wildcat will find oil.

In order to estimate the quantity of oil that will be found it is necessary to specify a second relation which gives the expected value of oil-in-place per discovery. The natural approach is to apply the lognormal hypothesis to describe the size distribution of reservoirs, and in this respect this model overlaps the first one. Putting together both components of the model, the probability of a discovery from the next wildcat times the expected size per discovery, given a discovery, yields the expected amount of crude to be found by the next wildcat.

How completely does this model specify the returns to exploration? Employing its postulated relation between discoveries of pools of a given size class and the number available and their areal extent, the model extrapolates the rate of decay in number of discoveries observed over successive increments of wildcats to forecast the limiting number of discoveries. With reference to the formulation we have used, no hypothesis is advanced regarding the initial determination of $N(w)/w$, the success ratio for drilling in the region (number of productive wells per wildcat drilled). Arps and Roberts made their projections of ultimate reserves by selecting values of the coefficient a which accorded with their experience about how much more successful drilling based on geophysical indicators was than random drilling. Crabbé, in reinterpreting the model for estimation purposes, treats a as an unknown, along with the ultimate number of fields in each size class. This coefficient is permitted to vary over time, and its values are estimated by an iterative procedure.[28]

What are the prospects of testing this model? If the knowledge-technology coefficient a is assumed constant, following Arps and Roberts, then there is no possibility of observing results like those shown by curves B or C of Figure 3. Hence, if such results were observed, the model would have to be rejected. Assuming a to be constant over any long period is unreasonable, however, since technology changes (perhaps erratically as a function of time), while knowledge of the geology of the region accumulates (presumably as a function of the number of wildcats drilled or some other variable which measures cumulative exploration effort). If a is permitted to vary, then any of the curves in Figure 3 is possible.

This type of model, in its present state, is essentially a projection model, designed to forecast trends in producing regions. What is its revelance to a newly opened region such as the Arctic? It will be many years before enough statistics can be collected to permit basing estimates of future returns to exploration on trends that have been observed in the successfulness of wildcat drilling. In the meantime, we might hope that studies utilizing the model will be made for mature producing regions, and that the model can be elaborated to provide some indication of how knowledge gained from mature regions can be applied to a new area in order to forecast the returns to exploration there.

FROM MODELS TO ESTIMATES OF EXPLORATION COSTS

The premise on which the two types of models just examined are based is that statistical regularities are to be observed in the occurrence of crude petroleum and other minerals. Some specific hypotheses, for example, that the size of reservoirs is lognormally distributed or that the spatial occurrence follows the negative binomial distribution, have been supported by empirical tests. The outcome of drilling a wildcat well cannot be foreseen, but if the possible outcomes can be described by a probability function, then statements can be made about the expected outcome and the likelihood of its falling within a given range. When returns to a larger drilling program are considered, the aggregate results can be predicted with greater precision than can the results of individual wells, a consequence of well-known statistical laws.

Ex ante information about the returns to exploration is necessary for the computation of the exploration component of long-run production costs, and it is this application of the statistical models that is of primary concern here. Each type of model offers promise for estimating the incremental returns to exploratory drilling. The Allais-type model seems better adapted to describing returns in a new basin where extrapolation of data from other areas must be relied upon. Moreover, the statistical properties of mineral occurrence that have been observed in connection with studies of this type of model make possible the use of sampling and estimation procedures which expand the usefulness of information obtained from the initial drilling results. The Arps and Roberts type of model aims at forecasting the returns to exploration over time in a particular area; it provides a mechanism for predicting changes in the returns as exhaustion effects begin to be felt. The Allais approach is silent with regard to the determination of the success ratio for exploratory drilling, a question raised by the second type of model. On the other hand, the Arps and Roberts model says nothing about the spatial distribution of hydrocarbon reservoirs, a question that arises in the context of the Allais model. In many ways the two are complementary.

For the purpose of forecasting the long-run cost of Alaskan crude, the Allais method of analysis appears attractive. To date production has been reported from three formations.[29] These results, together with data on experience elsewhere in the world where formations are similar, could lead to a forecast of the probable reserves to be found through further wildcat drilling. The initial estimates would require revision as more results became available.

The other papers in this volume provide estimates of unit cost, in cents per barrel of crude, for the lifting-plus-development portion of long-run cost. So far we have been concerned with returns to exploration; suppose someone with access to the drilling results had applied analytic techniques of the sort discussed to compute the expected volume of probable reserves to be found by the next fifty million, hundred million, etc., dollars spent on exploration. How could these figures be transformed into unit-cost estimates?

The problem of imputing to output a cost which covers investment outlays is dealt with in the other papers for the case of development investment. To compute such a cost it is necessary to postulate the time pattern of production in relation to the investment. The same condition applies to exploration cost estimates, but, unfortunately, the timing of production with respect to exploration investment presents a more complicated problem. With development investment it is frequently assumed that the timing of subsequent production is governed by physical laws which are summarized in production decline curves. These assumptions are upset, and allowances must be made, where regulatory constraints affect production rates. The timing of production in relation to exploration investment is determined by economic factors, in particular, decisions about the optimal level of the stock of probable reserves. Any imputation of unit cost must rest on assumptions about this desired stock, and we lack formal analysis of the problem on which to base such assumptions.[30]

As with other problems that are not transparent, approximations will have to be made until more rigorous procedures are developed. Given an indication of returns to exploratory drilling, one could estimate the investment needed to maintain a given stock of probable reserves under the pressure of a selected rate of crude output. This would permit imputing, in a rough way, a per-barrel exploration cost.

The temptation is constantly present to compare among areas the returns to exploration, measured as volume of reserves found per dollar spent. What counts in the end in determining the supply potential of any region is total production cost. To compare returns to exploration, ignoring development costs, is to risk very misleading predictions, just as the opposite is true, though perhaps less likely. Therein lies the importance of costing on a commensurable basis the various activities that together comprise petroleum production.

Since the bulk of this paper has been concerned with models of petroleum exploration, several concluding remarks are in order in regard to the promise and limitations of such models. The application to cost estimates emphasized here is only one of several possible uses. The models generate predictions about expected returns, and they also describe the variance of the returns. The magnitude of this variance is a reflection of the risks of exploratory drilling. Whether institutional arrangements function to minimize this risk would be an interesting question for study. Perhaps it is pointless to ponder further applications until the models themselves are improved, as surely they will be.

In their current state models of exploration appear to represent the statisticians' alternative to the geologists' evaluation methods. This apartheid of thinking ought not to persist. It was earlier suggested that the statistical models could be improved through a more careful geologic classification of the drilling data. This is by no means the only way in which they could be improved by inputs of geologic knowledge. In pressing on to the problem of forecasting where drilling will take place as well as how productive it will be, information on the number and quality of indicators of possible petroleum reservoirs in a region would be extremely valuable. It would be desirable, of course, to derive statistical exploration models from knowledge of the physical processes which determine crude petroleum occurrence. This has not been accomplished, although some writers have strengthened their results by showing that the statistical findings were consistent with plausible assumptions about those processes.[31] To the extent that various statistical hypotheses win confirmation, they may support particular geologic theories regarding the manner in which petroleum accumulations came into being and may afford new bases for insight.

NOTES

1. P. G. Bradley, *The Economics of Crude Petroleum Production* (Amsterdam: North-Holland, 1967).
2. M. A. Adelman, "Oil Production Costs in Four Areas," *Proceedings of the Council of Economics of the American Institute of Mining, Metallurgical, and Petroleum Engineers,* 1966, pp. 57-61.
3. P. G. Bradley, *The Economics of Crude Petroleum Production, op. cit.,* pp. 20-22.
4. This economic definition of proved reserves has been put forward by M. A. Adelman in *The World Petroleum Market, 1946-69* (to be published in 1970). For a discussion of the physical significance and method of measurement of proved reserves, see W. F. Lovejoy and P. T. Homan, *Methods of Estimating Reserves of Crude Oil, Natural Gas, and Natural Gas Liquids* (Baltimore: Resources for the Future—Johns Hopkins, 1965).
5. In a separate paper we hope to present a model which describes the optimal distribution of drillng effort among such categories as outpost wells or infield development wells, reco⁊nizing a two-dimensional (capacity, volume) characterization of proved reserves.
6. This is described in F. H. Lahee, *Statistics of Exploratory Drilling in the United States, 1945-1960* (Tulsa: American Association of Petroleum Geologists, 1962), pp. 1-2 and 132-135: or, alternatively, F. A. Dix, Jr., and L. H. Van Dyke, "North American Drilling Activity in 1968," *The American Association of Petroleum Geologists Bulletin,* 53 (June 1969), pp. 1153-1157.
7. J. J. Arps, discussion of the paper "What Are Petroleum Reserves?" by W. S. Eggleston, in *1962 Symposium of Petroleum Economics and Valuation* (Dallas: Society of Petroleum Engineers of AIME). Also in *Journal of Petroleum Technology,* July 1962, pp. 724-725. This and several similar classifications are discussed by Lovejoy and Homan, *Methods of Estimating Reserves of Crude Oil, Natural Gas, and Natural Gas Liquids,* pp. 57-65.
8. C. K. Leith, *Mineral Valuations of the Future* (New York: American Institute of Mining and Metallurgical Engineers, 1938), pp. 47-48. A summary discussion of the classification of mineral reserves is found in F. Blondel and S. G. Lasky, "Mineral Reserves and Mineral Resources," *Economic Geology,* 51 (November 1956), pp. 686-697.
9. Alberta (Province of), Oil and Gas Conservation Board, *Reserves of Crude Oil, Gas, Natural Gas Liquids and Sulphur, Province of Alberta,* Report 69-18, December 31, 1968, pp. 131-134, 142-145.
10. Dix and Van Dyke, "North American Drilling Activity in 1968," *The American Association of Petroleum Geologists Bulletin,* pp. 1157-1170.
11. M. A. Adelman, *The Supply & Price of Natural Gas,* supplement to the *Journal of Industrial Economics* (Oxford: Blackwell, 1962), pp. 3-4.
12. Note that this is not the net increase in probable reserves; to calculate the net increase, account must be taken of withdrawals as probable reserves are proved.
13. M. Allais, "Method of Appraising Economic Prospects of Mining Exploration Over Large Territories," *Management Science,* July 1957, pp. 285-345.

14. J. J. Arps and T. G. Roberts, "Economics of Drilling for Cretaceous Oil on East Flank of Denver-Julesburg Basin," *Bulletin of the American Association of Petroleum Geologists,* 42 (November 1958), pp. 2549-2566.
15. *Ibid.*
16. G. M. Kaufman, *Statistical Decisions and Related Techniques in Oil and Gas Exploration* (Englewood Cliffs, N. J.: Prentice-Hall, 1963).
17. R. G. McCrossan, "An Analysis of Size Frequency Distribution of Oil and Gas Reserves of Western Canada," *Canadian Journal of Earth Sciences,* 6 (April 1969), pp. 201-211.
18. More precisely, the random variable is barrels of crude initially in place. Barrels of probable reserves depend on the recovery factor, F in Figure 2, which we are treating as a given condition of the problem.
19. R. S. Uhler and P. G. Bradley, "A Stochastic Model for Determining the Economic Prospects of Petroleum Exploration over Large Regions," paper presented to the Canadian Economics Associaton, Toronto, June 1969.
20. Minor changes have been made in notation to maintain consistency.
21. In the cited work, tests with areal subdivisions of other sizes yielded essentially the same results.
22. See R. G. McCrossan, "An Analysis of Size Frequency Distribution of Oil and Gas Reserves of Western Canada," *op. cit.*
23. See Kaufman, *Statistical Decisions and Related Techniques in Oil and Gas Exploration op. cit.,* pp. 155-174 and 192-206.
24. Kaufman, "Statistical Analysis of the Size Distrbution of Oil and Gas Fields," in *1965 Symposium on Petroleum Economics and Evaluation* (Dallas: Society of Petroleum Engineers of AIME).
25. P. J. Crabbé, "The Stochastic Production Function of Oil and Gas Exploration in Mature Regions: Theory and Some Estimation Problems," paper presented to the Canadian Operations Research Society, Montreal, June 1969.
26. We have changed Kaufman's notation for the probability density function to $f(a;w)$ from $f(a,w)$ to emphasize that W is exogenuous.
27. Note that we are using "size" and "areal extent" interchangeably. In "Statistical Analysis of the Size and Distribution of Oil and Gas Fields," *op. cit.,* Kaufman discusses the assumption that petroleum yield per areal unit is constant and suggests how to generalize the model.
28. As Crabbé points out, if different values of a are allowed as drilling proceeds, it is no longer possible to compute a single estimate of $N(\infty)f(a;\infty)$, since there will be as many different values as there are values of a. He suggests the best estimate of $N(\infty)f(a;\infty)$ will be the one computed from drilling statistics for the longest observed interval.
29. *The New York Times,* December 12, 1969, p. 92.
30. This is one aspect of the problem mentioned in footnote 5 of this study.
31. See G. M. Kaufman, *Statistical Decisions and Related Techniques in Oil and Gas Exploration, op. cit.,* pp. 127-154.

Index

Adelman, M. A., 13–30, 100
Air shipments, cost of, 52
Alaska Division of Oil and Gas, 26
Alaskan oil: in competition with other areas, 25–27, 81, 90; finding costs and risks of, 23–25; impact on world reserves of, 19–20, 33–34, 80; reserves of, 19–20, 33–34, 80; importance of discovery of, 19–20, 33–34, 80; importance of discovery of, 13–28, 33–34, 80, 81; and taxes, 24, 26, 58, 63; see also North Slope; Prudhoe Bay oil field
Alaskan pipeline, 36, 67–68, 70; disadvantages of, 66; and terminal at Valdez, 36, 67, 72, 80, 88
Alberta Oil and Gas Conservation Board, 99, 106
Allais, M., 104, 106, 107, 111, 117
American Association of Petroleum Geologists (AAPG), 97, 99, 106
American Gas Association, 16
American Petroleum Institute, 16; on North Slope reserves, 17
Anderson, Robert O., 32–33, 38–39, 67, 80
Arabian American Oil Company (Aramco), 19
Arctic Ocean, 31, 32, 36, 52, 66; tankers on, 74
Arps, J. J., 98, 99–100, 104, 113, 115, 117
Atlantic Pipeline Company, 88
Atlantic Refining Company, 43
Atlantic Richfield Company, 8; and announcement of discoveries, 32–33; book value of, 43–44; and capacity of wells, 54; and cost of equity capital, 43; debt structure of, 50; earnings evaluation model for, 47–48; exploratory wells of, 79–81; and growth rate of earnings, 44–47; lease obligations of, 50; pipelines, 67, 88; and reaction of stock market, 38–40; and value of share of field, 65

Basins, 18, 31
Beaufort Sea, 52, 65
Bonus payments on leases, 11
Book value of stock, 41–44
Bradley, Paul G., 23, 93–119
British Petroleum, 40; and North Slope fields, 33; and pipelines, 67, 88
Brooks Range, Alaska, 31

Cabinet Task Force on oil import control, 79–81
California oil, development costs of, 21
Canada, pipeline across, 36, 66, 74–75
Capacity of wells, 54–55, 80; daily, 75; see also Reserves
Cape Simpson, 31
Capital: cost of equity, 40–49; and dividend valuation method, 41–44, 47–48; and Gordon and Shapiro method, 31–44, 47
Cash, discounted flow of, 9, 50–51
"Cat trains," 34
Chicago area, 36, 75; delivered cost of crude for, 89; transporting oil to, 36, 74–75
Competition with foreign crude, 25–27, 81, 90
Compulsory unitization, 26
Core holes, 31
Cost of equity capital, 40–49, 82; and discounted cash flows, 9, 50–51; and dividend valuation model, 41–44, 47–48; and earnings evaluation method, 44–48; and weighted average cost, 50–52; and weighted historical average for g, 44–47, 48
Costs: concept of economic, 24; defined, 9–10; of development, 9, 17–18, 21–24; of drilling, 21; effect of intensive development on, 17–18; of exploration, 11, 58, 83, 94; field development estimates of, 10; finding, 23–24; Maximum

123